THE CHANGING STRUCTURE
OF THE
MEAT ECONOMY

DALE E. BUTZ

Director of Economic Research, Illinois Farm Supply Company
Formerly Visiting Research Professor of Business
Administration, Harvard University

and

GEORGE L. BAKER, JR.

Assistant Professor, Marketing, Purdue University
Formerly Research Associate in Business Administration,
Harvard University

HARVARD UNIVERSITY
GRADUATE SCHOOL OF BUSINESS ADMINISTRATION
DIVISION OF RESEARCH
Boston · 1960

Library of Congress Catalog Card No. 60–11280

PUBLISHED BY DIVISION OF RESEARCH, HARVARD BUSINESS SCHOOL

PRINTED AT
THE PLIMPTON PRESS
NORWOOD, MASSACHUSETTS, U.S.A.

FOREWORD

DURING recent years much attention has been focused on the so-called agricultural problem or problems. While the problems have been of most concern to agricultural producers, other groups have had more than a passing interest in what has taken place or is happening "down on the farm." These farm problems and their solution have also been in the center of the political arena for many years. Even with all the interest, there seems to be little agreement on what the problems really are and even less agreement on what to do about them. Many people refer to the troubles besetting agriculture as if only agricultural producers or farmers were affected. The close relationship and interdependence existing among and between agricultural producers, marketing agencies, processors, suppliers, food retailers, and even consumers has been pointed out.[1] This concept, often referred to as "agribusiness," is spreading and gaining acceptance in many discussions of the so-called farm problem.

American agribusiness is so diverse that it almost defies description. The assets involved are several times those of General Motors, one of our largest industrial corporations. The number of products involved is staggering when compared to the output of vast industrial complexes. Because of the enormity and complexity of agribusiness, a systematic study of the component parts would seem to be more manageable than a detailed analysis of agribusiness in total. There are many ways in which agribusiness could be fractionalized for more intensive study. The method chosen was on the basis of broad commodity interests. The spotlight was first turned on

---

[1] John H. Davis and Ray A. Goldberg, *A Concept of Agribusiness*, Harvard Business School, Division of Research, Boston, 1957.

cotton and the future of this commodity. The cotton study [2] is followed by this report which delves into some of the problems of the livestock and meat economy with particular emphasis on beef and pork.

It is apparent that sweeping changes have occurred and will continue to occur in all segments of the livestock and meat industry. This is true whether attention is focused on the producer at one end of the marketing chain or on the retailer and consumer at the other end. Many excellent analyses have been made of particular areas or problems at all stages of marketing. Most of these studies have of necessity been based on the past. In a few cases projections have been made for the future, but these have been the exception rather than the rule. Practically all the previous studies have been concerned with problems or developments within one of the components of the livestock and meat economy. The report which follows represents the results of an attempt to select certain changes and then assess the impact of these changes on all segments or divisions of the industry. Problems of the industry are looked at in a somewhat different perspective from that used traditionally. Possible courses of action that might well be considered by the various firms and groups involved are also listed and discussed. Such an industry-wide analysis should be of interest to all the various business firms in the livestock and meat economy.

The basic work for this study was done in the academic year 1958–1959 while the authors were in residence at the Harvard Business School; Dr. Butz was on leave from Michigan State University and Dr. Baker from Purdue University.

The financial support for this study has come from two sources. The original endowment by Mr. George M. Moffett of a Professorship in Agriculture and Business at the Harvard

---

[2] Clifton B. Cox and Vernon W. Pherson, *The Competitive Potential of the U. S. Cotton Industry,* Harvard Business School, Division of Research, Boston, 1959.

Business School has been used in part for this research. The major support, however, has come from a gift in support of the Program in Agriculture and Business which was made to the School by the Whitehall Foundation. The School is grateful for this financial support which has made the study possible.

JOHN H. DAVIS
Former Director, Program in
Agriculture and Business

Beirut, Lebanon

business school has been used in part for this research. The major support, however, has come from a gift in support of the Program in Agriculture and Business which was made to the School by the Whitehall Foundation. The School is grateful for this financial support which has made the study possible.

James H. Davis
Former Director, Program in
Agriculture and Business

Beirut, Lebanon

PREFACE

THE PRIMARY PURPOSE of this report is to provide an analysis of pertinent data to assist the management of firms in the livestock and meat industry. We have described the present state of the meat economy as well as its immediate history, and have presented the data and reasoning on which we based our projections of the future. To some firms, or even whole segments of the industry, our projections may offer further justification for plans they have already made or objectives they have already set themselves. They may want to take further action or establish additional policies to cement their places or positions in the future. Others may view our interpretations and predictions with alarm as implying serious difficulties for their organizations. Segments of the industry or firms finding themselves in such a position must decide whether they will accept the future as inevitable and "just fade away" or determine whether there are aggressive countermeasures that they might take to improve their future opportunities and possibilities.

Our procedure consisted of two phases. First, we analyzed the published data on the changes that have occurred and are occurring in major sectors of the livestock and meat industry. We then had a number of personal interviews with research workers and trade representatives. These interviews were used not only as a check on our interpretations of the published data but also to sound out informal opinion on future developments in the industry. The research workers interviewed included personnel in the United States Department of Agriculture and the Land Grant colleges, as well as those on the staffs of farm organizations, meat packing companies, and marketing organizations. The trade representatives were management personnel other than research personnel at several different management levels in marketing organizations, meat packing and processing firms, and retail food firms.

The authors wish to acknowledge the assistance received from Dr. John H. Davis in the planning and initiation of this project and in reviewing the manuscript. The comments and keen insight of Professor Bertrand Fox, Director of Research at the Harvard Graduate School of Business Administration, made a significant contribution to the project at all stages of development. Mr. William Applebaum, Visiting Consultant on Food Distribution, and other staff members of the Harvard Business School offered suggestions and encouragement while the research study was in progress. Many specialists in the United States Department of Agriculture and our colleagues at Michigan State University and Purdue University unselfishly gave their time and ideas either in the form of interviews or manuscript reviews. Representatives of many firms in the industry were most cooperative in answering our questions. Many trade organizations and publications likewise were of considerable assistance in providing both ideas and data. Also, the granting of leaves of absence from Michigan State and Purdue Universities enabled the authors to spend a full academic year at the Harvard Business School.

The authors acknowledge the financial assistance, facilities, and other perquisites provided by the Harvard Business School. Miss Ruth Davison and Miss Constance Willard diligently typed the manuscript. Mrs. Dorothy Rowland provided editorial assistance, and Miss Ruth Norton, Executive Secretary of the Division of Research, was in charge of the details of publication. Special thanks are due our wives, Joyce and Alison, for their patience and inspiration.

While we are indeed grateful for all the assistance received, the final responsibility for the data and opinions presented rests upon the authors.

DALE E. BUTZ
GEORGE L. BAKER, JR.

Chicago, Illinois
Lafayette, Indiana

CONTENTS

LIST OF TABLES

LIST OF FIGURES

LIST OF APPENDIX TABLES

Chapter I

STRUCTURE OF THE MEAT ECONOMY

The Present

THE TERM "meat economy" embraces all firms involved in transforming feed, labor, live animals, and other inputs into meat products ready for consumer purchase or use. The route by which meat products eventually reach the consumer's table is not always the same. Livestock sometimes goes to the meat packer or processor directly, sometimes through a marketing agency. The meat is then delivered to retail food stores, hotels, restaurants, and institutions directly or through a wholesaler.

Most firms in the meat economy are independent, decision-making units. There are a few exceptions, however. A few producers slaughter, process, and merchandise their own meat products either as individuals or as members of a cooperative association. Some retail food companies do their own livestock feeding, slaughtering, and processing. A few meat packers and slaughterers also feed or contract for the feeding of livestock. And sometimes a firm performing one function in the meat economy is in effect in a "captive" relation to another firm that buys all or nearly all its output.

Perhaps recent changes that have resulted in the present state of the meat economy may best be understood in terms of the horizontal and vertical structure of the various firms it comprises. The horizontal structure is the set of relations between various firms performing the same function, for example, the relations of one meat packing company with another. Vertical structure refers to the relations between firms performing different functions, for example, the relations between livestock producers and meat packers, or between wholesalers and retailers.

The horizontal structure of the meat economy can be altered in at least three different ways. Two firms performing the same function can merge, or one can buy the other, a meat packer buying other meat packing companies, for example. The organization performing a particular function can change, as when chain stores began retailing operations formerly performed by independent grocers. Or the change can be in the concentration of business among the various firms, as for example, a decrease in the proportion of the total meat supply processed by the large packers.

These changes have taken place and continue to take place for many reasons. Economies of scale have certainly played a part both in the expansion of existing facilities of retailers and in the merging of two or more retail firms. Apparent diseconomies of scale have probably stimulated the increase in smaller meat packing plants. Changes in technology may create new functions or eliminate old ones. The development and widespread use of home freezers, for example, rapidly reduced the need for frozen food locker plants. Changes in demand either for products or for services may create new organizations or radically change existing ones. The demand by restaurants for ready-to-cook portion-controlled meat cuts has spurred the growth of very specialized wholesalers who can meet these exacting specifications. Changes in horizontal structuring might also come about through government regulatory action.

Vertical relations too are subject to change. The desire or need for controlling the quantity or quality of supplies has frequently led to closer integration. An attempt by one functional level to improve its bargaining position with relation to another sometimes leads to further integration. And sometimes integration is the most expeditious way for particular functional groups to obtain capital, management help, or other necessary inputs and services.

Perhaps the most potent force for change in either the horizontal or the vertical structure since World War II has been the change in relative bargaining power. Earlier the meat packers and processors had been the dominant force in the industry. A large proportion of the output was produced by a small number of firms, and these firms were very large compared with the sellers of livestock on the one hand and the buyers of meat on the other. At one point the meat packing and processing firms even controlled transportation facilities and retailing outlets.

With the advent of the large retail food chains and the formation of voluntary and cooperative retail groups, the competitive relation between the meat packer and the retailer has changed. Better informed producers with larger volumes of output, and larger, better managed marketing organizations have changed the relation between the meat packer and the livestock seller.

Even within the meat packing and processing industry itself competitive relations have changed. Relatively small independent beef slaughtering plants have been set up in many parts of the country. Several smaller pork processing plants have developed specialized products. As a result some of the beef and pork market has been taken away from the large national packers.

The Future

It is difficult to predict the future of the meat economy in detail. New technology and improvements in efficiency may call for the formation of new firms or entirely new segments of the industry. Present firms may become obsolete as a result of technological advances or improvements in efficiency made by new firms.

Even without these improvements, changes in the use of resources may come about when one segment of the economy operates at relatively low efficiency. Not only new firms but also firms from other segments may take over the functions of the inefficient firms. In livestock feeding operations, for example, it might be found that a different combination of resources would yield a higher return than the present system. Feeding might be done by feed companies, meat packers, or retail food companies. This is not to say that the more efficient system will invariably be put into operation, for the more efficient firm may have better alternative uses for its resources. In addition, public opinion, fear of government action, or other nonmonetary reasons may deter the potentially more efficient firm.

There are no indications that the bargaining power struggle in the livestock and meat economy will be any less strenuous in the years ahead. In fact, it seems entirely possible that several of the groups making up the meat economy will have to intensify their efforts to achieve bargaining power if they hope to maintain or expand their position in the industry. Other groups will find that their relative bargaining power has increased with little apparent effort on their part or in spite of their actions to the contrary. The final chapter on the shift in bargaining power in the livestock and meat economy has not been written, but there are some straws in the wind that indicate the general direction of the changes.

In the following chapters we shall discuss in more detail the future changes expected in the structure of the meat economy. Whether these changes take place or not depends in large part upon the attitudes and the relative bargaining power of the various segments comprising the meat economy. In the final analysis, however, the changes that take place will depend most of all upon changes at the consumer level as these are reflected through the marketing channels to the producers. It is with the consumer then, that our analysis begins.

Chapter II

THE EXPANDING CONSUMPTION OF MEAT

THE ULTIMATE objective of the meat economy is to supply consumers with meat products in the form and at the time and place desired. In addition, these products must be supplied at a price that the consumers are willing to pay. Food, which makes up about 21% of total personal consumption expenditures in the United States, obviously competes with many other items for the consumer's dollar. Likewise, meat, making up 25% to 30% of the consumer's food expenditures, faces competition from other foods. Also, within the meats, one kind or species or cut may be a substitute for another kind, species, or cut.

During recent years there has developed throughout the American business community an increased appreciation of the necessity of gearing the production and marketing system to consumer demand. Consumer demands and preferences for meat and meat products are ever changing. Some of the changes arise from external forces such as changes in population, population mix, or income. Other changes are induced by the agencies serving consumers within the meat industry through advertising and promotion, by changes in products, or by other means.

Exports of meat and meat products from the United States approximately balance imports of similar products into the United States. Both exports and imports are very small, however, compared with total meat production and consumption.[1]

[1] See Appendix Table 1 for a detailed breakdown of meat imports and exports, 1950–1957.

Therefore, total meat consumption is approximately equal to total production.[2] There is, of course, a variable time lag between production and consumption while the products are moving through the marketing channels. The close relationship between meat production and consumption means that per capita consumption fluctuates very closely with changes in the meat supply, particularly in the short run. In the longer run, however, consumer demand does have a significant influence on production, and hence, upon the supply of meat of various types available.

Total and Per Capita Consumption

Total meat consumption in the United States has more than doubled since 1900. Furthermore, the consumption of the different types of meat over the same time period has varied considerably. From 1950 to 1957, for example, beef consumption increased 49.4%, lamb and mutton increased 19%, veal increased 23%, and pork consumption stayed about the same.[3]

Between 1950 and 1957, the total population of the United States increased from 151.7 million to 171.2 million—an increase of approximately 13%.[4] During the same period, the total consumption of red meat rose from 21.7 billion pounds to 26.8 billion pounds, the per capita consumption rising from 144.6 pounds to 159.0 pounds in 1957 (see Table 1). Total per capita red meat consumption declined in 1958 and then began to increase again in 1959 as both the cattle and hog cycle moved into stages of higher production and marketings.

[2] See Appendix Table 2 for data on production and consumption of meat products, 1950–1959.
[3] U. S. Agricultural Marketing Service, Statistical Bulletin No. 230, *Livestock and Meat Statistics, 1957* (Washington, Government Printing Office, July 1958), pp. 283–284.
[4] See Appendix Table 3 for U. S. population data 1950–1958.

Per capita consumption of poultry continued to increase steadily during this period. Although the effect of poultry market developments on red meat consumption has not been isolated, there is no question that as poultry consumption has increased, poultry meat has been substituted for red meat. Most of the increase in red meat has been in the consumption of beef, per capita consumption having risen from 63.4 to

Table 1. Per Capita Consumption in Pounds of Red Meat and Poultry, 1950–1959

	Beef	Veal	Lamb & Mutton	Pork (excluding Lard)	Total Red Meat	Poultry *	Total Red Meat & Poultry
1959 †	81.0	6.7	4.4	66.0	158.1	35.6	193.7
1958	79.7	6.8	4.1	60.6	151.2	33.9	185.1
1957	84.5	8.8	4.2	61.5	159.0	31.5	190.5
1956	85.4	9.5	4.4	67.4	166.7	29.8	196.5
1955	82.0	9.4	4.6	66.8	162.8	26.4	189.2
1954	80.1	10.0	4.6	60.0	154.7	28.1	182.8
1953	77.6	9.5	4.7	63.5	155.3	26.7	182.0
1952	62.2	7.2	4.2	72.4	146.0	26.8	172.8
1951	56.1	6.6	3.4	71.9	138.0	26.1	164.1
1950	63.4	8.0	4.0	69.2	144.6	24.7	169.3

* Chicken, including broilers and turkey.
† Forecast.

Source: *Livestock and Meat Situation*, November 1958, p. 6; March 1959, p. 12.

81.0 pounds. Since 1940, pork has been becoming a smaller and smaller percentage of the total meat supply. In the early 1950's pork represented almost 50% of the total red meat consumption; by 1958–1959, the figure had fallen to just slightly over 40%.

The decline in the demand for pork and the increased demand for beef may be accounted for in many ways. In recent years, the public has become increasingly calorie conscious and increasingly fearful of a possible association of animal fat in-

take with heart disease. As a result, relatively less pork is eaten
at home and in restaurants.[5] The urbanization of many rural
families has probably changed their eating habits and led to a
reduction in their consumption of pork. Retailers, becoming
more aware of the waste and shrink of various kinds of meat,
have favored those with less shrink and waste. When packaged, many meats may be more appealing than pork so that
with the increasing use of prepackaged meat,[6] pork sales may
have suffered proportionately.

Form of Meat Consumed

There has been a change not only in the distribution of species of meat consumed but also in the forms in which it has
been consumed. In the spring of 1955, fresh and frozen cuts
combined accounted for only 50% of all meat consumed by
the families surveyed by the U. S. Department of Agriculture
(see Table 2). Since such meats averaged slightly higher in
price than processed meat they represented a larger percentage
of the total value of meat—54%. The processed meat consumed was mostly ground beef and cured pork. Since processed meats have little further loss from bone and trim at the
table, the amount of processed meats expressed on the basis
of edible meats exceeded the consumption of fresh and frozen
meats.

Although comparable data for earlier years are not available,
there is evidence that processed meats have grown in relative
importance.

Such an uptrend is in keeping with the tendency to add
more processing, packaging, and preparation to all foods.
Processing of meat also allows quality to be more nearly

[5] P. Luby, "Declining Demand for Pork—Reconsideration of Causes and
Suggested Prescription for Remedy," *Journal of Farm Economics*, Vol. XL,
No. 5, December 1958, pp. 1832–1838.
[6] See Appendix Tables 4 and 5 for increases in self-service meat departments.

Table 2. **Kind and Form of Meat and Meat Products in the Meat Diet, All U. S. Households,* One Week in Spring, 1955**

	Quantity Used (pounds)		Value (dollars)	
	Per Person	Percentage of Total	Per Person	Percentage of Total
Kind of Meat				
Beef	1.25	41.4	.77	42.5
Veal	.08	2.6	.05	2.8
Lamb & Mutton	.09	3.0	.06	3.3
Pork	1.14	37.8	.67	37.0
Variety Meats	.10	3.3	.05	2.8
Luncheon Meats	.36	11.9	.21	11.6
Total Meat	3.02	100.0	1.81	100.0
Form of Meat				
Fresh & Frozen	1.52	50.3	.97	53.6
Processed Meats	1.50	49.7	.84	46.4

* Meats used at home.

Source: U. S. Agricultural Marketing Service, Bulletin No. 249, *Consumption Patterns for Meat*, by Harold Breimyer and Charlotte A. Kause (Washington, Government Printing Office, May 1958), pp. 8, 10.

standardized, and it is adapted to the use of trademarks and brands, facilitating company identification and advertising. For these reasons, many packers have been interested in expanding their markets for processed meats, and have repeatedly introduced new products.[7]

Factors Contributing to Changes in Meat Consumption

There are several factors in addition to production and population which influence per capita consumption over the long run. The primary factors—income, price, and population mix —are discussed here. Attempts to expand the market for meat by the firms in the meat economy either as a group or individually must take these factors into account.

[7] Breimyer and Kause, *Consumption Patterns*, p. 9.

Income

The food consumption studies made by the United States Department of Agriculture in 1955 and other similar studies [8] indicate that families with higher incomes consume larger quantities of meat than do lower income families (Figure 1). This relation between income and quantity consumed or expenditures for consumption is referred to as income elasticity.

Figure 1

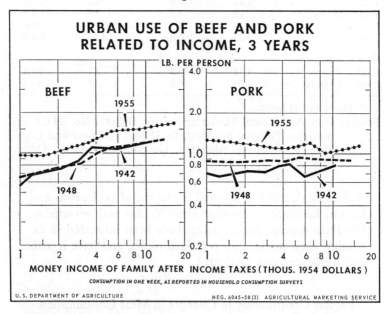

Income elasticity (based on quantity) for all meat is approximately 0.35. That is, a 1% increase in real income—income after price changes are taken into account—would be expected to result in approximately a 0.35% increase in the quantity of meat consumed.[9] The income elasticities (quan-

[8] See Appendix Table 6 for household expenditures for meat by household income groups in 1956.

[9] Estimates of elasticities in 1959 made by specialists of the U. S. Department of Agriculture in correspondence with the authors.

tity) vary for different species and cuts of meat; they are estimated at approximately 0.4 for beef, 0.25 for pork, and 0.6 for lamb.[10] A larger increase in consumption of lamb than either pork or beef can therefore be expected for each added dollar of real income. The income elasticities calculated on the basis of expenditures are somewhat higher than elasticities based on quantity of meat. The income elasticity (expenditure) for all meat approximates 0.45. For the various species, income elasticity (expenditure) approximates 0.5 for beef, 0.8 for lamb and mutton, and 0.35 for pork.[11]

The difference between the income elasticity calculated by expenditures and by quantity indicates that increases in real income increase the amount of money spent for meat more than the quantity of meat consumed. Apparently, as real income increases, consumers purchase higher priced cuts of meat, better quality meat, or kinds of meat that include more service costs.

There are indications that the income elasticity for meat calculated on the basis of quantity purchased is declining.[12] As incomes in general rise, the basic wants of consumers with respect to the quantity of meat are more nearly satisfied. Income elasticity (expenditure) is likely to remain relatively high as consumers continue to purchase higher priced meat and more built-in services. For farm food generally Cochrane has suggested that the income elasticity (quantity) is about 0.20 but that it will probably be zero by 1975, and certainly will be zero by the year 2000. He also suggests that the expenditure income elasticity will remain at about 1.0 because food services will continue to be purchased as income rises.[13]

These data suggest that opportunities for increasing meat

[10] *Ibid.*
[11] *Ibid.*
[12] U. S. Agricultural Marketing Service, Bulletin No. 96, "Price Elasticities of Demand for Nondurable Goods, with Emphasis on Food" by Richard A. Foote (Washington, Government Printing Office, March 1956), pp. 23–25.
[13] Willard Cochrane, *Farm Prices—Myth and Reality* (Minneapolis, University of Minnesota Press, 1958), p. 87.

consumption through programs designed to increase incomes of consumers are limited, for there may be a time when the basic farm food wants of American consumers are all satisfied. The long-run trend in meat consumption has been up. But the percentage of disposable consumer income spent for meat has not increased even though consumers have increased the amount of services purchased with meat. Immediately after World War II when supplies of some consumer goods were relatively short compared with supplies of meat and other food products, a somewhat higher percentage of disposable income was spent on meat. Since meat had been rationed during the war years, the lifting of restrictions also resulted in an upsurge in consumer spending for meat. Since that time, however, the retail value of red meat consumed expressed as a percentage of disposable income has moved downward.

Some of the decline may have been a readjustment to more normal levels after the postwar high; some may also be attributed to the fact that meat prices did not rise as fast as the prices of other commodities. Rising incomes, coupled with relatively lower meat prices, meant that consumers could buy the same or larger quantities of meat with a smaller percentage of the food dollar.

In 1955 there were many families and individuals in the United States (15 million people) with incomes of less than $1,000. Various food distribution programs were suggested for these persons. Cochrane concludes that although these programs would (1) increase modestly the over-all food consumption of the average members of the low-income groups, (2) seek out and eradicate those relatively few cases of hunger or serious malnutrition where they now exist, and (3) make a modest contribution toward strengthening and maintaining the aggregate demand for food, they would not actually increase the aggregate demand for food very much.[14]

[14] Cochrane, *Farm Prices*, p. 153.

Price

Another important factor affecting meat consumption is the price of the product. Usually as prices go up, consumption decreases and vice versa. The ratio of a change in quantity to a change in price is called price elasticity. The figure is negative because the changes in price and quantity are usually in opposite directions. The price elasticity of all meats is approximately −0.6.[15] In other words, a 1% change in price would be expected to result in a change of about 0.6% in the opposite direction in quantity consumed. Stated another way, a 1% change in quantity would be expected to result from a change of more than 1% change in price in the opposite direction. While these relations are generally held to be true in the short run (year to year or within the year), Working discovered that in the longer run, the demand for meat at retail also seemed to be elastic (−1.2).[16]

During the period 1953–1958, the price indices of meat, chicken, and fish as a group were lower than either the indices for all foods or the consumer price index.[17] The declining percentage of the consumer's dollar spent for beef and pork during this period indicates that the relatively lower prices did not increase consumption rates appreciably: consumers took only about the same or a slightly greater quantity of meat products. There are various estimates of the effect changes in meat prices have on consumption. In 1955, when there was a large supply of meat, it was found that relatively large decreases in price were needed to move relatively small increases in supply into the hands of consumers. Over a longer time span, without the press of a glutted market, perhaps

[15] R. C. Kramer, R. A. Goldberg, and J. H. Davis, "An Agribusiness Appraisal of the Meat Economy," unpublished manuscript, Division of Research, Harvard Business School, Boston, Massachusetts, May 1957, p. 35.

[16] E. Working, Demand for Meat (Chicago, Institute of Meat Packing, 1954), p. 87.

[17] See Appendix Table 7 for index of consumer prices for meat, chicken, and fish, all foods consumed at home, and consumer price index, 1950–1957.

prices would not have to be relatively as low in order to move such large supplies of meat into consumption channels. Should there be a point when the basic farm food needs of consumers are fully met, price reductions would have to be substantial in order to move larger quantities into consumption channels.

Population

Increases in the total United States population have created an expanding market for meat. The rate of increase in population was approximately 1.5% per year for the decade prior to 1956, and has since increased to 1.6% per year. This rate is expected to increase to 1.7% in 1959 and then gradually decline to 1.3% in the middle 1960's.[18] These changes in the rate of population growth reflect the changes in the number of women of child-bearing age as a result of the high birth rate of the late 1920's and 1940's and the low birth rate of the 1930's.

Following World War II there have been changes in the make-up of the population that have affected meat consumption. The number of births each year from 1950 to 1958 has been at a record high. People have been marrying at an earlier age, and women have been bearing children at an earlier age.[19] Advances in the medical field have led to increasing numbers of babies surviving and increasing numbers of older people.

The two groups, people over 65 and children under 10, consume small quantities of meat compared with other age groups. The households with teenagers spend the greatest amount for meat (Table 3). The growth in the number of households with teenagers will therefore tend to increase the demand for meat during the first half of the 1960's.[20]

Most of the change in total meat consumption in the fu-

---

[18] "The Future Population Mix," *Fortune Magazine*, February 1959, p. 97.
[19] *Ibid.*, pp. 95 and 96.
[20] For distribution of the population by age groups, see Appendix Table 8.

Table 3. Household Expenditures for Meat by Stage in the Life Cycle of Household Head and Children, One Year, 1956

Stage in Life Cycle	U.S. Households Percentage of Total	Percentage of Total Expenditures for All Households				Average Expenditure per Household			
		Fresh *	Frozen †	Canned ‡	Total	Fresh	Frozen	Canned	Total
No children, head under 40	8%	6%	5%	7%	13.3%	$148.00	$1.20	$4.20	$153.40
Children under 10	40	44	51	44	44.7	214.00	2.20	5.20	221.40
Children 10–19 years only	16	21	21	17	21.1	253.00	2.30	5.10	260.40
No children, married, head over 40	23	22	17	26	22.0	181.00	1.30	5.30	187.60
No children, single, head over 40	13	7	6	6	6.9	110.00	.80	2.20	113.00
Totals	100%	100%	100%	100%	100%	$194.00	$1.80	$4.80	$200.60

* Fresh meat, meat products, and dishes.
† Frozen meat, meat products, and dishes.
‡ Canned and jarred meat, meat products, and dishes.

Source: *Life Study of Consumer Expenditures,* Supplement (New York, Time Incorporated, 1958).

ture will be the result of increases in population, not changes in per capita consumption rates. Rising consumer incomes will have only a limited effect on per capita consumption. Substantial price decreases seem unlikely, particularly in view of the services to be added to the products. The changing of the population mix to include relatively more teenagers in the early 1960's will tend to increase the per capita consumption. Between 1965 and 1975, there will be an increase in the proportion of the aged and the very young, that will decrease the per capita consumption of meat. Therefore, increases in the per capita consumption of meat by 1965 or 1975 are likely to be modest in nature.

Future Consumption

A few years ago great concern was expressed over the so-called "fifth plate" or expected 25% increase in food needs. Since that time, however, it has become clear that agricultural producers could fill the "fifth plate" and more.

Table 4. Per Capita Food Consumption of Livestock Products, Selected Periods 1925 to 1956 and Projections for 1975 (1956 = 100)

	Average 1925–29	Average 1951–55	1956	Projected 1975	
				I*	II†
Meat Animals	82	92	100	108	114
Dairy Products	93	99	100	105	108
Poultry	54	91	100	114	118
Eggs	91	104	100	99	99
Total	83	95	100	107	111

* The first price level (I) is fairly close to levels (1956) for farm products as a whole.

† The second price level (II) is approximately world prices for major export crops and feed grains with livestock prices related through historic product-feed price relations.

Source: Daly, "Prospective Demands," p. 113.

Daly calculates the 1975 per capita food consumption of all livestock products at between 7% and 11% above the 1956 level (Table 4). The per capita consumption of meat animals over the same period is estimated to increase between 8% and 14%. The lower estimates are calculated on the basis of 1956 prices for agricultural products. The higher per capita estimates are based upon somewhat lower agricultural prices than existed in 1956.[21] In his projections for the future Daly also makes the following assumptions:

1. There will be peace and a high level of employment.

2. Population will grow rapidly—193.5 million in 1965; 230 million in 1975.

3. Output per worker will rise.

4. Real income per person will be 40% higher in 1975 than in 1956.

5. General price level in 1975 will be at about the 1956 average.

Daly estimates that by 1975 domestic utilization of all livestock products will increase to 50% over 1956; and utilization of meat animals will increase 47% to 56% (Table 5). Since imports are expected to increase somewhat faster than exports, he predicts that the 1975 utilization will require an increase of from 40% to 46% in production of all livestock products.

Since the above consumption projections were made, the Bureau of the Census has revised its population estimates for 1975, predicting 235 instead of 230 million people. The higher population estimate raises Daly's figures by 2% to 3%: The domestic utilization of meat animals in 1975 should, therefore, be about 50% higher than in 1956, assuming that prices stay at the 1956 level. If, however, livestock prices are lower,

[21] R. F. Daly, "Prospective Demands for Food and Fiber," in Subcommittee on Agricultural Policy, Joint Economic Committee, *The Policy for Commercial Agriculture, Its Relation to Economic Growth and Stability*, 85th Cong., 1st Sess. (Washington, Government Printing Office, November 1957), Sect. II, pp. 108–118; see also analyses by James Bonnen and others in this section.

with lower estimated world prices for export crops and feed grains, meat animal consumption can be expected to rise about 58% by 1975.

Projections have not been made of the future relative importance of the various species in the expanded total meat consumption. It seems likely, however, that beef production

Table 5. Domestic Utilization of Livestock Products, Selected Periods 1925 to 1956 and Projections for 1975
(1956 = 100)

Item	Average 1925–29	Average 1951–55	1956	Projected 1975 I*	Projected 1975 II†
Domestic Utilization	64	92	100	144	150
Food	58	90	100	146	152
Meat Animals	58	88	100	147	156
Dairy Products	66	94	100	143	148
Poultry	38	87	100	156	161
Eggs	64	99	100	136	136
Nonfoods	116	104	100	120	126
Exports	43	65	100	62	62
Imports	83	112	100	161	161
Production Required	63	90	100	140	146

* The first price level (I) is fairly close to current levels for farm products as a whole.

† The second price level (II) is approximately world prices for major export crops and feed grains with livestock prices related through historic product-feed price relations.

Source: Daly, "Prospective Demands," p. 114.

and consumption will continue to grow at a faster rate than pork production and consumption. This prediction is based upon the apparently greater income elasticity of beef and a seeming consumer preference for it. The difference in the rate of growth will tend to narrow between now and 1975, however, as hog producers and others associated with the hog market strive to improve the quality of pork products. In addition, pork prices are likely to be somewhat lower relative to beef prices and thus be an incentive for increases in the consumption of pork. Poultry meat consumption will continue to expand but probably not at as rapid a rate as during the 1950's. The consumption of lamb, mutton, and veal will fluctuate with supplies but will tend to remain a relatively small part of total meat consumption. The consumption of processed meats will continue to increase at a modest rate. Widespread use of technological advances, such as quick freezing and new packaging techniques and materials, may reduce the proportion of meat sold in processed form between 1965 and 1975. We are of course defining processed meat narrowly, to exclude frozen or differently packed fresh meat products.

The Place of Food Purchases

Concurrent with the changes in the total and per capita consumption of meat, changes have been taking place in the proportion of meat eaten inside and outside the home. It is very difficult to compare the value of meat consumed in the home, with the value of that reaching consumers via hotels, restaurants, and institutions.

Home produced food has not been sold; therefore its value has not been established. Expenditures by consumers in hotels, restaurants, and institutions cover costs of preparation and serving as well as the costs of the food itself. For the most part, statistics on the pounds of food moving through these channels are not available. In order to make valid comparisons of the amounts of meat and food products moving through the various outlets, all data have been converted to an estimated retail value basis, the value the same food would have attained had it been sold at retail through grocery stores.

One of the most significant changes in the retail value of food consumption since World War II has been the decline in the relative amount of home-produced food consumed. The continued decline in the number and percentage of farm families was responsible for the major part of the decline. Rising income levels, increased numbers of women working away from home, increased availability of food products at seemingly reasonable prices, and other factors also had an effect in reducing the home production of food. In 1957 an estimated 8% of all food consumed was home-produced, and about 5% of all meat consumed was home produced. During the late 1930's and the World War II years, between 15% and 19% of all food consumed was produced at home.

The retail value of food consumed through hotels, restaurants, and institutions, sometimes referred to as on-premise consumption, increased from 9% of total food consumed during the depression to a peak of about 18% during World

Table 6. Estimates of the Percentage of Retail Value * of Total Food and Meat Consumption by Source, 1958 †

		Food		Meat
Consumption at place of purchase				
Public restaurants		12%		17%
Private restaurants		2		3
Institutions and travel agencies		3		3
Total			17%		23%
Consumption *not* at place of purchase				
All retail stores		69%		69%
Grocery stores	50%		57%	
Government		2		2
Manufacturers, hucksters, etc.		5		1
Total			76%		72%
Consumption at place of production			7		5
Total			100%		100%

* Estimated market value of food: at place of purchase, 24%; not at place of purchase, 71%; at place of production, 5%.
† Partial data 1929–1957 in Appendix Table 9.

Source: Total figures for food consumption from unpublished data of Marguerite Burk, Head, Consumption Section, Statistical and Historical Research Branch, U. S. Department of Agriculture. Meat consumption at place of production from correspondence with Marguerite Burk. Consumption of food and meat through grocery stores from "What the Public Spends for Grocery Store Products," Topics Publishing Company, New York, 1958. All other figures are approximations by the authors.

War II. On-premise consumption declined to 15% in 1950 but subsequently gradually increased to almost 17% in 1957.[22] It is estimated that about 17% of all food and about 23% of all meat was purchased for on-premise consumption in 1958 (Table 6). The estimate for meat is higher than for all food in that relatively more meat and better qualities of meat are consumed by diners eating away from home.

The above estimates for all foods and for meats purchased for on-premise consumption are lower than those reported by the restaurant and institutional trade. The popular estimate used by the trade is that approximately 25% of all food consumed is accounted for by restaurants and institutions. Differences arise because the estimates in this report adjust the consumer expenditure data (market value) to an adjusted retail value basis and also include home-produced food as a part of total consumption. The differences in the estimates for meat probably can be ascribed to differences in the types of food outlets included and in the statistical techniques employed.[23]

Public eating places, hotels and restaurants, account for about two-thirds of the on-premise food consumption. The remaining one-third is about evenly divided between private eating places and institutions. As a result of the growth of in-plant feeding, increased enrollment in schools and colleges, and the increased numbers of patients and old people in hospitals and other institutions, the amount of food consumed in institutions has been increasing.

Along with the changes in the place of consumption there also has been an apparent shift in the species of meat being purchased by eating places. *American Restaurant Magazine* reported that restaurants are shifting toward more beef, veal, and poultry and away from lamb and pork.[24]

[22] Annual data may be found in Appendix Table 9.

[23] See "The Institutional Market for Food Products" *Institution Magazine*, Chicago, Illinois, 1958.

[24] "American Restaurant Subscriber Analysis," *American Restaurant Magazine*, Chicago, Illinois, 1958.

Table 7. Food Consumption through Grocery Stores Relative
to Total Food Consumption, 1947–1957

| Year | All Food | Fresh Meat | | | | Frozen Meat | Canned Meat | Fresh Poultry | Fresh Fish | Fresh and Cured Meat Fish, and Poultry |
		Beef	Pork	Veal	Lamb					
1957	48%	51%	62%	50%	94%	41%	70%	54%	89%	58%
1956	46	48	59	47	90	42	70	51	85	55
1955	46	48	58	47	88	41	70	50	85	55
1954	45	46	56	44	85	41	69	48	85	52
1953	44	46	58	45	84	39	69	47	85	52
1952	41	40	64	43	85	38	68	46	87	50
1951	41	40	65	41	83	40	70	44	86	49
1950	39	37	57	36	77	37	68	42	82	45
1949	39	42	53	37	76	36	68	34	84	45
1948	37	38	48	33	69	—	67	34	—	43
1947	36	37	48	33	68	—	69	33	—	41

Source: Paul E. Olsen, Director of Marketing Research, Topics Publishing Company, Inc., New York.

Approximately three-fourths of all food is purchased for off-premise consumption. Between 1945 and 1957 off-premise consumption, expressed as a percentage of the retail value of all food consumed, increased 10 percentage points. The decrease in the use of home-produced food during this period was about equal to the increases in food sold for off-premise consumption. Most of the off-premise consumption is accounted for by food purchases from grocery stores. The percentage of all food purchased from grocery stores increased from 36% in 1947 to 48% in 1957 (Table 7). As grocery stores have gained in relative importance as a source of food and meat, purchases by consumers from other retailers and directly from manufacturers, wholesalers, and hucksters have declined. This relative decline was particularly true for meat. Also, government purchases have remained relatively stable at about 2% of total food and meat since World War II.

In summary, since World War II consumption of home-produced food decreased 9%, on-premise consumption decreased 1%, and off-premise consumption increased 10%.

The Future

The major change in the future place of purchase for consumption will probably be a relative increase in on-premise consumption because of expanded industrial in-plant feeding, more leisure time, longer vacations, more travel, and rising consumer incomes expected in the future. Grocery stores and other retail outlets will make an effort to capture an increasing share of the consumer food market by supplying foods containing more built-in services such as precooking. In spite of these efforts, the proportion of total food and total meat consumed away from home will expand by 1975 when possibly 20% to 22% of all food and 25% to 27% of all meat will be consumed away from home. By 1975 the purchase of food and meats through grocery stores is expected to rise to 65%.

Chapter III

RETAIL BUYING PRACTICES

RETAIL MEAT buyers have been very influential in their dealings with meat suppliers and are likely to become even more so in the future as retail stores and companies become fewer in number and larger. The expected large meat supplies in the early 1960's and the consequently well-stocked packers' coolers probably will further weaken the packers' bargaining position in relation to the retail buyers. Retail buyers are likely to be in a position where they are going to need, demand, and get market service. If one plant or firm does not give them what they want, they will go to another, or perhaps even supply it themselves.

The increasing influence of the retailers in the meat economy is pointed up by changes that have occurred in the buying of meat. Perhaps the most significant changes have been (1) a substantial reduction in the number of retail meat buyers and a consequent increase in the quantities of meat purchased by the average buyer, (2) the widespread use of increasingly precise specifications for meat bought by retailers, (3) the increasing numbers of retailers buying on a specification basis, (4) the changing buying methods of chains and independents, and (5) the growing ability of retail buyers to get the meat they desire. Before we discuss these points, we shall summarize briefly the increasing importance of the retailers in the meat economy.

The Increasing Influence of the Retailers

The period since World War II has been characterized by an increase in the market influence of food retailers relative to other components of the meat economy. The increasing influence of retailers has centered around changes in the size and type of store and in the size and type of company. The supermarket has emerged as the primary outlet for groceries and meat. Some of these supermarkets have become so large that even as a single unit they can achieve many of the economies of large-scale buying. Chain store companies and groups of independent retailers have represented an increasing share of total food sales.

Changes in Size and Type of Store

Prior to the depression of the 1930's almost all grocery stores would have been classified as small stores. The appeal of the supermarket to consumers as a self-service, cash and carry, low-priced, complete food store led to the growth of supermarkets relative to other sizes of food store. In the period 1952 to 1958, sales through supermarkets increased from 44% to over 68% of total grocery store sales. In 1958 the average volume of sales per supermarket was over $1,100,000.[1]

The number of small stores, which has declined for several years, will probably continue to decline, though at a much slower rate, and is likely to stabilize at about 125,000 stores in the early 1970's. These stores will continue to serve small towns and communities as convenient food stores.

By 1975 there will be approximately 45,000 supermarkets (stores with annual sales of $375,000 or more), representing between 20% and 25% of all grocery stores and between 85% and 90% of total grocery store sales. There will be approximately 30,000 superettes (stores with annual sales between

[1] "Facts in Grocery Distribution," *Progressive Grocer*, annual editions, 1953–1959.

$75,000 and $375,000), which will make up nearly 20% of all stores and about 10% of sales. Small stores (with annual sales less than $75,000) will number around 125,000 or about 60% of all stores. These small stores will handle only about 3% of all grocery store sales. These increases in store size are related to changes in the size of retail company.

Increasing Size of Retail Company

Chains

Since the end of World War II, chains have experienced a gradual increase in their percentage of total grocery store sales and in the percentage of total grocery stores. In the six-year period, 1953 to 1958, the percentage of grocery store sales through chain stores increased from 39% to 45%. Even though the percentage of all grocery stores that were classified as chains increased from 1953 to 1958, the actual number of chain stores declined approximately 2%.[2] Over the same period the number of chain companies declined 10%. These increases in sales along with declines in the number of stores and companies represent a strengthening of the chains as a group relative to other retailers.

Increases in sales of chain stores and the reduction in store numbers resulted from the growth of chain supermarkets relative to other types of chain stores.[3] Chains have been conducting extensive refurbishing and building programs eliminating or expanding small stores and building large stores.

Affiliated Groups

The retail food organizations showing most rapid growth from 1948 to 1958 were the affiliated independent groups. While a few affiliated groups were formed in the early part of the century, their rapid growth came after the chains had become an important factor in food retailing.

[2] *Ibid.*   [3] *Ibid.*

In order to compete better with the chain stores, independents took on many of the characteristics of chains. Through pooling their purchases by means of wholesaler-sponsored voluntary groups or retailer-sponsored cooperative groups, the independents were able to receive the quantity discount which had previously been available only to the chains. Affiliated groups enjoy some advantages that chain stores do not have: for example, lower taxes in total, fewer labor problems, relatively greater freedom from government interference, and perhaps greater management incentive. The disadvantages center around the difficulty of enforcing policy decisions and possible organizational instability.

Voluntary Groups. Affiliated groups are of two kinds: the wholesaler-sponsored voluntary group and the retailer-owned wholesaler or cooperative group. The large federated groups of voluntary wholesalers were founded in the 1920's. In 1956 the three largest federated groups represented a total of approximately 184 voluntary wholesalers and 13,000 retailers.[4] These three organizations represented approximately one-fourth of all independent sales in 1956. As was true of the chains, the number of stores in these voluntary organizations are decreasing in number and growing in size.

These large federated organizations represent large numbers of stores and a large proportion of independent sales, but the amount of control these organizations can and do exercise over their wholesaler and retailer members is limited. The retail stores are franchised by the wholesaler with a contract that may be terminated in thirty days by either party.

Because of the difficulties of enforcing controls on the wholesalers and retailers, federated organizations may have an increasing number of problems in the future. Also, as these federations were primarily built around the superette or small

[4] "Supermarketing USA, 1957," *This Week Magazine*, 1958, and *Voluntary and Cooperative Group Magazine*, April 1959, p. 41.

supermarket, they may experience increasing difficulty in carrying on a program for these smaller merchants as well as the new large supermarket operators. Often when a superette or small supermarket operator obtains a large store, he no longer feels that he needs the federated group. For these reasons the federated voluntary organizations may decline in importance in the future and have smaller retailers as members.

Cooperative Groups. In cooperative groups stock is purchased by the members (retailers) who receive patronage refunds based on annual purchases of merchandise. This type of organization has many advantages and disadvantages compared with voluntary organizations. The advantages center about the fact that the retailer owns the wholesaler and thus has a voice in determining the policies and services that the wholesaler will provide.

Cooperative group wholesalers average larger in sales volume than voluntary group wholesalers.[5] Cooperative wholesalers also sell to fewer stores than voluntary groups, for cooperatives both sell to larger stores and sell more to the stores they service.[6] Cooperative retailers have increased sales 226% over the decade 1948 to 1958, a much greater percentage increase than either the chains or voluntaries.

Unlike the voluntary groups, many of the newer cooperatives have developed around serving large retail stores. Cooperative groups' wholesalers also have lower gross margins than the voluntaries. Cooperative groups will, therefore, increase in sales volume relative to the voluntary groups. The relative sales of affiliated groups as a whole will probably remain stable at the 1958 figure of 44% of total grocery store sales.

[5] "Facts in Grocery Distribution," 1959 Edition, *Progressive Grocer*, p. 19.
[6] Unpublished survey, *Progressive Grocer*, 1959.

Increasing Use of More Precise Specifications

Both the proportion of meat bought under specification and the preciseness of the specification have increased during recent years. In this text specification buying is defined as "the exercising of a rigid control over the quantitative and qualitative characteristics of a given [meat] item by the purchasing firm." [7] There is, of course, wide variation in the way the control is achieved. The control may be achieved through written contracts, oral gentlemen's agreements, or more often by a mutual understanding established through practice and custom.

Three conditions are conducive to increased and tighter specification buying by retailers:

1. Where there are possibilities of and the desire for improvements in uniformity and standardization of meat, that is, where retailers want as nearly as possible the same quality and weight of carcasses or cuts of meat week after week.

2. Where there is a need for closer checks and controls on cutting procedure. Since carcasses or wholesale cuts that are uniform in size and quality yield nearly the same amount of retail cuts, butchers in the store could be checked more easily.

3. Where there is a desire by the retailer to merchandise meat with specifications, such as "corn-fed" or "specially trimmed" beef, as a means of differentiating his meat.

The following conditions are not conducive to tightened or increased specification buying:

1. When price spreads between and among qualities and types of cuts vary. Tight specifications on a particular kind of meat might not be desirable if the price of that kind of meat varied sharply in comparison with closely substitutable kinds of meat.

2. When there would be extreme difficulty in determining

[7] W. T. Kelley, "Specification Buying by the Large Retailer," *Journal of Marketing*, January 1954, p. 255.

and maintaining the tighter specifications of a particular retailer.

3. Where the retailer is not interested in merchandising a differentiated meat product.

Beef

The specifications for meat purchases are determined mainly by the type of meat the retailer feels that the customers want and the cut-out yield obtained through the retailer's cutting practices.[8] Some stores follow specific cutting procedures, some age beef (which requires carcasses with a higher degree of fat covering), others have greater or less consumer demand for specific types of cuts so that retail margins on these cuts may vary between stores of the same company. With specification buying the companies are able to standardize cutting procedures and establish comparable margins on all cuts for all stores.

Although many companies have buying specifications, these specifications vary between the companies. Some retailers specify the weight range of the carcass, sex of the animal, fat trim, conformation, and other characteristics. While each retailer interviewed maintained that he had not tightened up his specifications in recent years, each one felt that on the whole the market was moving in that direction. There was some evidence that specifications for individual companies were becoming more precise in spite of what the meat buyers reported.

Many companies, particularly those located near slaughtering facilities of packers, select and mark their carcasses on the rail in the packer's cooler. The packers interviewed said that there was less of this kind of selling than formerly. In view of the decline of branch house merchandising, this change seems likely. Formerly, many relatively small retailers selected their meat at the nearby packer branch house. Representatives of one major chain organization indicated that they were con-

[8] Interviews with trade representatives.

vinced that the only way they could get the kind of meat they wanted was to select it in the packer's cooler. Other retail representatives were not happy with the meat they were getting but were not unhappy enough to select it themselves from the cooler of the packer. Many large retail companies have meat warehouses where specifications for beef can be checked centrally, giving the retailers an opportunity to enforce more precise specifications.

Pork

Retail buyers agree that quality differences are less readily apparent in pork than in beef. Almost all of them were skeptical about the ability to judge the quality of pork products, especially internal fat. Many felt that lack of this ability was a limiting factor in the effective use of any kind of grading system or other quality differentials on pork products at the retail level.

Several retail representatives indicated that they either had tightened, or were going to have to tighten, specifications on fat thickness and size of the loin eye for pork loins. Representatives of one organization interviewed said that they purchased only lean, squared pork loins with a minimum of 4 square inch loin eyes for a premium of about 3 cents per pound. Several buyers expressed an interest in merchandising so-called meat-type pork if they could be assured an ample supply of products of a consistent quality.

The general attitude among the retailers interviewed was that improvements in the quality and standardization of pork products were desirable, but these retailers did not feel that they were the ones to initiate such changes.

Standing Orders

For all meats the use of a standing order with packers was more common than the number of formal contracts would indicate. A standing order almost of necessity calls for the use of some sort of buying specifications by the retailer.[9] While a few chains have written standing orders, the most common practice is to have an informal agreement under which suppliers know the approximate tonnage that they can expect to sell to a particular retailer each week.

Increased Specification Buying

As the size of chains has increased, the number of chains using specifications for meat buying has also increased because of the need for standard uniform meat products. Specifications are used to facilitate control by central headquarters over meat buying, cutting, advertising, and merchandising. There is evidence that many retailers are insisting upon quality specifications over and above U. S. or packer grades. The independents, too, are increasing the use of specifications so that they may buy and sell more standardized meat products. Interviews with the sales representatives of the meat packers revealed that in general independent meat buyers are less discriminating than their chain counterparts; on the other hand, many independent retailers select their meat personally. As independents grow in size, the need and desire for buying on a specification basis increases.

Perhaps the largest increase in specification buying has come with the growth of affiliated group meat programs. Until 1955 few grocery wholesalers handled meat for their retail accounts. In order to serve their retailers as one-stop wholesalers, voluntary groups first, then cooperatives, started meat programs. These programs strive to standardize the meat throughout the affiliated group and thus utilize specifications more than the retailer did buying individually. Representatives of many groups anticipate a rapid expansion of their meat buying pro-

[9] While many people did not admit it when first questioned, further questions brought this fact out. This was due to the difficulty in defining a standing order.

grams. The growth and success of the meat programs by the affiliated groups also have induced some unaffiliated wholesalers to offer this program.

In 1958, 29% of the voluntary and 17% of the cooperative wholesalers handled meat (Table 8). Wholesalers handling meat do not necessarily handle all kinds of meat nor do they necessarily service all their member stores with meat. The Federal Trade Commission reported that 24.5% of the voluntary

Table 8. Percentage of Grocery Wholesalers Handling Meat, 1955–1958

Year	Voluntary	Cooperative	Unaffiliated
1958	29%	17%	16%
1957	25	19	7
1956	25	12	5
1955	18	11	N. A.

Source: "Facts in Grocery Distribution," *Progressive Grocer*, 1957 and 1958 editions; and unpublished survey by *Progressive Grocer*, 1959.

wholesalers and 19.4% of the cooperative wholesalers provide meat purchasing services, but only 17.6% of the voluntary group stores and 18.3% of the cooperative group stores received the service. The wholesalers are currently going through a period of experimentation with meat programs. Once this period is completed there will probably be a considerable increase in the number and the size of meat programs.

Meat Buying Practices [10]

There is no one general pattern that adequately describes the buying practices of all or even of a majority of retail stores.

[10] The following discussion is in part based on U. S. Agricultural Marketing Service, Marketing Research Report No. 298, "Economic Effects of U. S. Grades for Beef," by Willard F. Williams et al. (Washington, Government Printing Office, January 1959) which includes a summary of retail buying practices of almost all of the larger retail food chains as well as a good number of independent retailers; and in part on interviews with key people in the trade and with research personnel.

The chains employ practices and procedures different from the independents. Voluntary or cooperative group buying is in many respects similar to the buying by chain operators. Buying practices of one chain or one independent often vary greatly from practices employed by other chains or independents in the same area. Despite the differences, however, some general observations are justified.

Although special pricing arrangements, such as discounts and rebates, are occasionally present *sub rosa*, nonprice incentives [11] are frequently used by suppliers to lure retail accounts. The extent to which such incentives are used is not known. There were indications that larger retail companies took advantage of these nonprice incentives more than smaller retail companies.

Chains

Usually suppliers call the meat buyer on a given day and quote prices for meat meeting the specifications set by the chain. The buyer usually waits until he has received several calls before making an order so that he has the "feel" of the market, and then places an order for delivery the following week.

In general, the practice of buying ahead ("forward purchasing") by chains is practical. In most cases, the price is determined at the time of sale, in which case price risks are passed on to the retailer if the packer has a firm commitment on the livestock. Although retailers generally have the right to refuse

[11] E.g., guaranteed display payments, free displays with merchandise purchase, store name listing in consumer ads, prepaid shipments, free goods, cooperative advertising, in-store display material, store manager contests, premiums with quantity purchases, store demonstrations, deals, display contests, free research, payments for special display, payments for position of shelf, movement of goods analysis in competing stores, case allowances, prepriced merchandise, suggested price advertising, mat service, free recipe and menu service, performance contracts, swell allowance, label allowance, exclusive distribution rights, free in-store assistance.

a delivery, apparently in the past they rarely exercised this right even when the price had declined.

Chain stores generally buy under one or a combination of the following methods: [12]

1. Central merchandising—where there is central planning, buying, pricing, and controlling of stock, with stores simply selling what they are sent.

2. Central purchase with store requisitions—where central buyers purchase and warehouse stock and store managers requisition goods for drop-shipment to the stores.

3. Price agreement plan—where central buyers decide on what the stores may buy and the terms of purchase, but where the decision as to how much and when to buy is left to the stores.

Many chain companies find it advantageous to buy centrally for all their stores. While this is a common practice for regional, local, or what might be considered small chains, national chains usually do not buy centrally for all stores. Many national chains or chains operating over a wide geographical area are organized so that the buying function is exercised in whole or in part by regional buying offices. A Department of Agriculture survey of 28 chains reported that the amount of meat purchased per buying division by large chains was less than the amount of meat purchased per buying division by medium-sized chains (Table 9). In a given region, therefore, the medium-sized chains may be in a stronger buying position than the large chains.

Sometimes store personnel are allowed to purchase a limited number of items on an individual store basis. Chain representatives expressed the opinion that the present decentralization of the meat packing industry tended to reduce the advantages gained from central purchasing by national offices.

[12] John W. Wingate, *Buying for Retail Stores* (New York, Prentice Hall, 1956), p. 77.

The flexibility of regional purchasing, plus savings in transportation costs and the opportunity for a fresher, better quality product, favor more decentralized buying. In some cases chains have only partially decentralized their buying by giving regional offices instructions to fill as many as possible of their needs locally.

Specialization among meat packers and processors affects the buying process. The retailers handle a wide variety of prod-

Table 9. Total and Average Number of Buying Divisions, Average Volume per Buying Division, and Average Total Volume per Firm by Size of Chain Company, 1955

Size of Chain Company*	Number of Companies	Buying Divisions	Average Number of Buying Divisions per Company	Average Volume per Buying Division (1,000 lbs)	Average Volume per Firm (1,000 lbs)
Small	16	18	1.1	5,650	6,356
Medium	8	16	2.0	25,249	50,499
Large	4	64	16.0	10,859	173,750
Total	28	98	3.5	12,252	42,882

* Small, 0–19 million pounds of beef; medium, 20–99 million pounds of beef; large, 100 million or more pounds of beef.
Source: Williams, "Economic Effects," p. 118.

ucts, both fresh and processed. It is almost imperative for the chains to patronize a number of suppliers in order to get a complete line of the qualities, brands, and products desired. Retailers also cannot ignore the fact that certain meat packers and processors have developed a reputation in particular lines and that many packers' brands have large consumer acceptance.

Some chain meat buyers are former packer employees and have in a sense been trained by the meat packing industry. This means that these buyers have an intimate knowledge of the economic factors associated with meat packing operations. Other chain companies have packing plants of their own or have livestock custom slaughtered to satisfy part of their total meat needs. Through these means these chains have, or have access to, the actual costs of some of the packing operations.

Representatives of the suppliers report that buyers for retail food chains are in a sense harder to deal with than other types of retail buyers. The chain buyers are usually better informed, have a better idea of what they want, and because of the quantities involved are in a better position to bargain than independent retail buyers. Even though the chains are often hard to deal with, most of the suppliers welcome their business because of the large volume of the orders. Larger volume may enable the suppliers to reduce unit costs by spreading fixed costs over a large output; in turn, the buying cost per unit may be lower for the buyer with the large volume. The representatives of meat packing and processing firms pointed out that most chain buyers make a sincere effort to get as nearly as possible the quality and kind of meat desired at the lowest possible price.

In general, the chain companies buy a higher percentage of their meat from national packers than do independent retailers (Table 10). This is probably because many of the chains can buy carload lots of particular meat products and some have warehouses in which to store them. While these warehouses are principally for storage, many of them also include trimming, breaking, bacon slicing, and other processing operations. A Super Market Institute study reports that as the volume of firms moves above twenty million dollars annually it becomes advantageous to have a grocery warehouse; [13] the volume at which it becomes advantageous to build a meat warehouse is perhaps somewhat larger. Not only the sales volume, but the location of the retail outlet with respect to meat suppliers and the availability and proximity of private or supplier warehouse facilities, must also be taken into account.

Although relatively few chains had meat warehouses in

[13] See Appendix Table 10 for details of warehouse ownership.

1958, the advantages of having meat warehouses will become more pronounced as the volume of grocery firms increases.[14] In 1957 approximately 50% of the meat sales of chain store companies with annual sales over fifty million dollars passed

Table 10. Percentage of Beef Purchases by Source of Supply, Type of Grading, and Government Grades, Chain and Independent Retailers, 1955

	Independent	Chain
Source of Supply		
Retailer packinghouse	—	5.3%*
Independent packer	48.5%	41.5 *
National packer	36.4	50.0 *
Meat wholesaler	15.1	3.2 *
	100.0%	100.0%
Type of Grading		
Federal Graded	72.8%	93.6%
Packer Graded	14.7	5.1
Ungraded	12.5	1.3
	100.0%	100.0%
Federal Grades		
Prime	6.4%	.6%
Choice	70.3	84.0
Good	17.2	8.1
Commercial	5.0	3.5
Other	1.1	3.8
	100.0%	100.0%

* Weighted average.
Source: Williams, "Economic Effects," pp. 97, 99, 105, 120, 123, 126.

through their own meat warehouses.[15] The decline in the number of packer branch houses in many areas of the country also may stimulate warehouse ownership by retailers as a means of assuring an adequate supply of meat.

There are several reasons for a retailer to acquire a warehouse; (1) he may get better terms by buying carload shipments to go to the warehouse rather than smaller shipments

[14] See Appendix Table 11 for percentage of stores buying from wholesalers by size of store.
[15] Harvard Business School, Division of Research, Bulletin No. 148, *Operating Results of Food Chains in 1957*, by Wilbur B. England.

for the individual stores, (2) trained inspectors at a warehouse could determine and assure the quality received, (3) the retailer could better schedule deliveries to the stores from a warehouse than could several suppliers or packers, (4) more sources of supply would be available when delivery is to a warehouse rather than to stores,[16] (5) the warehouse could provide a location where meat could be fabricated—partially trimmed and "broken down" into wholesale cuts.

As the size of the wholesaler increases, the possibilities for having meat warehousing increases. *Progressive Grocer* reported that in 1958 over 40% of the independent grocery wholesalers with annual sales of over ten million dollars handled meat.[17] Although the term "handle" does not mean warehouse, the opportunity for warehousing meat is certainly greater if the wholesalers are handling meat in some other way. Thus, as the size of retail companies increases, as more chains are developed, and as affiliated groups expand meat programs, there are likely to be an increasing number of retail meat warehouses.

Independent and Small Chain Stores [18]

The buying practices of the independent retailers and smaller chain stores are similar to the practices of the larger chains with a few important exceptions. The smaller stores carry a higher percentage of ungraded meat, lower grades of meat, and packer graded meat (Table 10). Also, the independent stores, because their purchases are smaller, buy a slightly greater percentage of their meat supplies from meat wholesalers than do chain stores.

In the sample interviewed by the U. S. Department of Agri-

[16] *Super Market Merchandising*, April 1959, p. 53.
[17] *Progressive Grocer*, Unpublished Survey, 1959.
[18] Retailers with an annual volume of less than three million pounds of meat. The U. S. Department of Agriculture beef grading study previously cited used this definition, therefore some chain organizations are included in this section.

culture approximately one out of every four retailers selected his beef in the packer's cooler. Most of the other retailers inspected the meat on delivery and could send it back to the supplier if it was unsatisfactory. Meat was seldom shipped back to the suppliers, however. In general, the independent retailer relies heavily upon federal or packer grades and on personal relations with the supplier for assurance that he will receive the quality of meat he wants.

Independent retailers sell a wider range of qualities of meat than the chain retailers. A smaller percentage of the independent stores handle choice grade and a larger percentage handle good and commercial grade than do large chain stores. And, independent stores handle a higher percentage of prime grade than chain stores (Table 10).

In many of the smaller retail stores, meat buying is not a specialized function but a part of the duties of the store manager, the head of the meat department, or other store personnel with varied responsibilities. It is only natural that such nonspecialized personnel lean very heavily on their suppliers for information on price, quality, and sometimes even quantity to be purchased.

A complaint of retail buyers was that the organization of the sales department of major packers did not mesh well with their retail buying organizations. One retail buyer may have to deal with several packer representatives in order to buy all the meats for which he is responsible. For the larger retail accounts the packer may have a coordinator assigned; too often, however, he has no authority with respect to the product or price. Hence, he must check back with the management before reaching a decision. The smaller packers, on the other hand, usually have one person in touch with the retail buyer, and this person, since he usually is in a position of authority, can readily make adjustments regarding price, products, or terms.

Affiliated Groups

Larger volume purchases by groups of independent retailers should provide some price advantages in buying. A more important advantage perhaps is the fact that affiliated groups can afford skilled personnel to help members directly in buying meat and in improving their knowledge and skills in buying and merchandising meat. It is often charged that packer sales representatives merchandise some of the poor quality meat products through small independent stores. A group buying organization ought to correct this practice or at least help the store personnel identify the quality of meat they are buying or should buy.

While the meat programs of the various affiliated groups are similar, they do vary in the way the meat is purchased. In one large federated [19] group the wholesaler's meat representative collects the orders from the retailers and settles the price and quantity with the packer of his choice. Once the representative has settled on price and quantity, he calls the federation headquarters and reports the order. The federation office then sends a "selector" to the specified packing house to select and roll the meat with the federation label. The meat is then shipped to the wholesaler or directly to the store, with the meat billed to the wholesaler. The wholesaler, in turn, sends the retailer a bill for the actual cost of the meat plus a small service charge along with his periodic grocery bill.

Another federated group relies on the packer representatives to select and ship the meat according to the specifications of the order. Under this arrangement the federation does not enter into the buying directly. The federation supplies a brand to roll the meat and provides general supervision for the meat program. There are many different arrangements with respect to the autonomy of the group members. Some organizations

---

[19] Federated groups are organizations made up of voluntary wholesalers and their retail accounts, such as, Independent Grocers Alliance, Red and White Corporation, and Clover Farms.

have a very tight policy restricting the products an individual store can buy on its own. In others, the stores are free to buy anything individually if they think they can do better than by buying through the group.

Apparently many of the advantages of a meat program have not been recognized by group retail members. This may be due in part to the belief of many retailers that they know meat as well as their wholesaler, and therefore need no help in buying and merchandising. It may also be due in part to the independent retailers' reluctance to let the wholesaler become further involved in the operations of the retail store. Furthermore, the usual charge of cost plus one cent per pound may seem high to the retailer. Undeniably, some of these reactions are justified.

Vertical Integration

While the primary function of food retailing is that of merchandising goods and services to consumers, some retail organizations are heavily engaged in wholesaling, processing, and slaughtering meat. In some cases the retail organizations actively participate in the production of livestock either by direct ownership or on a contract basis. At one time the typical small store was very highly integrated in that many products sold in the store were produced by the store owner. With the growth of the food retailing industry, the control over products and services shifted from the store to independent suppliers.

Wholesaling

Chain companies represent integrated operations in that they assume functions previously performed by wholesalers by buying direct from manufacturers for shipment to their stores or warehouses. The affiliated groups are also examples of wholesaler-retailer integration. Here the retailers and wholesalers are tied by ownership in the case of cooperative groups and by contracts in the case of voluntary groups.

Approximately 90% of grocery store sales and over 50% of grocery store meat sales are accounted for by some type of integrated retail-wholesale organization. As the meat programs of the affiliated groups become more widely established, the percentage of meat purchased by integrated organizations will increase. As the chains and affiliated groups increase sales relative to unaffiliated retailers, larger percentages of both meat and total sales will be purchased by integrated organizations. As one trade magazine predicted, ". . . the grocery industry may soon be run about entirely from the central headquarters of voluntary and cooperative [groups] and corporate chains." [20] Large partially integrated organizations may find it desirable and possible to integrate further.

Processing

Food retailers have not moved rapidly into meat processing operations. Many retailers have carried processed meat items under their own private label, which in most cases were processed for the retailers on a contract basis. A few retailers have their own facilities, chiefly for processing bacon and other pork products in which freshness is an important factor.

In general, retailers handle packer-branded processed meat items in addition to those under their own label. In this way, the retailers capitalize on the advertising of the national brands by appealing to consumers who shop for such brands, and at the same time also merchandise large quantities of their own labeled product, which may be selling at slightly lower prices than the national branded products.

As the number of packer branch houses declines, and the meat wholesalers remain relatively specialized in fresh beef operations (see Chapter IV), the processing of meat, particularly pork, by retailers may increase. This increase would chiefly be in the processing of meat in which freshness is a very important factor and where the establishment of processing fa-

[20] *Super Market Merchandising*, April 1959, p. 47.

cilities requires a relatively small capital expenditure. Pork curing and canning, for example, are not likely to be carried on by retailers. Even with these projected increases in the processing facilities of retailers, a very high percentage of the processing will still remain in the hands of the large packers.

As retailers increase the number of their meat warehouses, they increase opportunities for processing meat themselves. Although the warehouses are primarily for the storage or fabrication of beef (not considered as processing under the Department of Agriculture definition), the additional investment required to go into processing would be much smaller than if the retailer were starting from scratch.

Slaughtering

The number of food chains owning and operating federally inspected livestock slaughtering plants declined from 11 in 1950 to 7 in 1955 (Table 11). These were chiefly cattle killing establishments. Other studies reported that several chain and independent retailers carry on nonfederally inspected slaughtering operations to fill at least part of their meat needs.

Many of these slaughtering operations were started during

Table 11. Food Retailing Companies Engaged in Federally Inspected Slaughter and Numbers of Livestock Slaughtered, 1950–1956

Year	Companies	Number Slaughtered
1956	7	861,595
1955	7	789,511
1954	10	508,361
1953	11	544,357
1952	11	476,223
1951	11	479,981
1950	11	512,584

Source: U. S. v. Swift & Company, "Brief by the United States in Support of Motion for Summary Judgment," Equity No. 37623 in U. S. District Court for the District of Columbia, p. 26.

World War II in order to assure the stores of having ample quantities of meat of desired qualities during the war shortage. With more ample supplies of meat in the years following the war, the need for such operations on the part of the chains lessened. For various reasons, however, some food retailing firms have continued their slaughtering operations: (1) slaughter plants were purchased during the war and have continued to be profitable operations; (2) executives are intensely interested in and have a keen knowledge of meat slaughtering; (3) an adquate consistent supply of the meat desired cannot be obtained through other means; (4) chain executives can obtain data on the cost of packing; (5) the slaughtering operations provide a lever for bargaining with other packers when buying. Many executives of chain companies have said that they would rather not be in the meat packing business as long as they can get the desired service from someone else. If such service cannot be obtained, however, some chain organizations will go into meat packing again.

The four large chains included in the U. S. Department of Agriculture study [21] drew about 63.5 million pounds of beef from their own slaughtering establishments. One of these chains did not sell any of the beef slaughtered in its own plant in its retail stores. Of the other three chains, the largest supplied only 5% of its own beef, the second largest supplied 30%, and the smallest supplied all of its own beef.

Two of the food chains that slaughter cattle also operate cattle feedlots, although these feedlots supply only a small portion of the total kill.[22]

> The trend seems to be for food chain slaughterers to buy fewer cattle in public markets and more in the feedlots as they are needed for immediate slaughter. Contracting to take

[21] Williams, "Economic Effects," pp. 124, 125.

[22] R. C. Kramer, "Cattle Feeding by and for Packers and Retailers," a report to the research director of The Fact Finding Committee of the American National Cattlemen's Association, July 1959, pp. 10 and 16.

delivery appeared to be more important for food chains than the purchase of feeders and having the feeders custom fed.[23]

Feeding

Feeding by chain companies is more common in the western part of the country than in other areas. Food chains that own feedlots do so chiefly for flexibility. The chain operators report that the kinds of cattle they need are not always available at reasonable prices. Livestock placements in these kinds of feedlots generally provide fat cattle during seasons when they are in shortest supply.

The number of cattle fed by chains has decreased from almost 70,000 head in 1954 to approximately 25,000 head in 1957.[24] Except for 10,700 sheep fed in 1954 by one chain company, no livestock other than cattle were fed by chains in the four-year period, 1954–1957. As a part of the feeding by chains is geared to chain slaughter facilities, it is not likely to increase unless the slaughtering facilities increase. A rise in the numbers of packers and feedlots in the western areas will also reduce the need for feeding by chains.

The current trend toward a greater use of private labels by retailers along with the reluctance on the part of large packers to supply this type of meat could force the retailers to integrate in order to obtain the desired meat products. It is likely that many private label meat products will be supplied to retailers by specialized meat suppliers under contract.

Vertical integration by retailers has come about partly because retailers were dissatisfied with the product, price, margin, or service obtainable from meat suppliers. As the products and services were not provided by other functional levels, the retailers sought to obtain them through direct ownership or on a contract basis. Some retailers wanted greater control over

[23] Correspondence with R. C. Kramer.
[24] U. S. Agricultural Marketing Service, Packers and Stockyards Docket #16, "Feeding Operations of Meat Packers" (Washington, Government Printing Office, September 1958), p. 6.

supply or quality and integrated to insure the desired control. This need for control over supply was the apparent cause of retailer-owned packing plants during World War II. Opportunities for a return on investment at other functional levels in the marketing of meat that is greater than that obtained from strictly retail operations would stimulate further integration. Although the likelihood is slight, more integration may occur as the country becomes more saturated with retail food stores.

In summary it can be said that food chains currently do only a small part of the total processing, slaughtering, and feeding and therefore have a negligible effect on national livestock and meat prices. Meat processing operations of retailers will probably increase slightly, but will be limited by the increased processing by packers and meat wholesalers. It is not likely that there will be further expansion in livestock slaughtering by retail food companies. The investment is large, the return has been low, and the trend has been away from it. Livestock feeding operations by retail food companies will also become less important. Integration or the threat of integration will be used by retailers largely as a means of forcing the rest of the meat economy to satisfy the desires of the retailers.

Future Buying

In the future retail buyers will want more uniformity in size, quality, and conformation of the carcass with less waste and trim and a higher percentage of tender, lean meat. They will want to buy in larger quantities from as few suppliers as can adequately fill their needs. If the selling organization of the packer does not fit the structure of the retail buying organization, it will probably be the packer who will have to change.

Retail buyers will raise more questions than their predecessors about the variations in quality and price that occur regularly in meat production and marketing. This may lead retail buyers and the retail food industry to look for ways to reduce the instability of the industry. It is more likely, however, that the retail food industry will seek out and support those organizations that they feel will fight this battle for them.

A case in point seems to be the situation that has existed with pork. The retailers have been concerned about pork quality and sales, but they have not done a great deal about it. Several of the retailers interviewed pointed out that they have been waiting for somebody (packers, marketing agencies, and producers) to give them a consistently superior pork product that is easily identifiable in the consumer's eyes as being different from past or other existing pork products. In fact, it is the packers and the processors who must make effective use of price incentives and aggressive merchandising if a differentiated pork product is to be sold by retailers.

Practically all of the meat to be sold at retail will be purchased by some kind of group buyer—either chain or independent. This means that the buying function will be in much stronger hands. For the most part these buyers will be well informed as to quality, price, and other considerations and will know what they want.

It is unlikely that many retailers will make *formal* contracts with meat packers regarding the sale or delivery of specified quantities of meat for current or future delivery. Retailers are skeptical of formal arrangements chiefly because of the possibility of government action against them, but also because of the possibility of public resentment. There will be a growth of informal agreements, however, which are very similar to contracts in effect although not as binding. This informal type of arrangement is likely to grow and develop to the point where a firm can expect a given amount of business from a particular organization each week provided price is in line and the quality specifications are met.

ABSTRACT

THE CHANGING STRUCTURE OF THE MEAT ECONOMY

It is apparent that sweeping changes have occurred and will continue to occur in all segments of the livestock and meat economy. This study represents an attempt to select certain of these changes and then assess their impact on all segments or divisions of the industry. Problems of the industry are looked at from a somewhat different perspective than that used traditionally. Possible courses of action that might well be considered by the various firms and groups involved are also listed and discussed. Such an industry-wide analysis should be of interest to all the various business firms in the livestock and meat economy.

This publication is the third evolving from studies conducted at the Graduate School of Business Administration, Harvard University, under the auspices of the Program in Agriculture and Business. The basic research for this study was done in the academic year 1958–1959 while the authors were in residence at the Harvard Business School; Dr. Dale E. Butz was on leave from Michigan State University and Dr. George L. Baker, Jr., from Purdue University.

The meat economy has been and will continue to be characterized by the multiplicity and everpresence of change in the organization of the industry, in its technology, and in the demands of the consumer.

Consumer demand ultimately determines the development of the industry. As a result of consumers' increasing patronage of chain stores and independent supermarkets, retailers have taken or assumed a position of relatively greater bargaining power, both because of the large volume of business they handle and because of their increasing ability to fulfill the functions of other segments of the meat economy. Consumer demand in conjunction with improvements in technology has resulted in increased availability of meat products.

With expected rises in income and population, 50% to 60% more meat will be consumed in 1975 than in 1956. Livestock production is expected to keep pace with or outstrip this increase in consumption, so that there will be a buyers' market. Research on new or changed products may help to increase the proportion of consumer expenditures going for meat and meat products. Technological advances will make quick-frozen cuts more important, improve ways of identifying meat quality in live animals and meat products, and perfect processes to increase shelf life of meats.

In 1959 chain store companies handled about 22% of all the meat consumed. The figure will probably rise by 1975. Increased purchases of meat by voluntary and cooperative groups and grocery wholesalers are expected. Buyers will therefore be fewer in number, each buying larger quantities of meat.

Retail buyers will seek more uniform, differentiable products and will therefore be buying larger quantities of meat on a specification basis above U. S. or Packer Grade. The retail buyer's newly increased bargaining power will enable him to demand and get production, delivery, packing, and sometimes even prices he wants.

In the wholesale sector, the major changes have been a decline in the importance of the branch houses of national packers, a large increase in the quantities of meat products shipped directly to retail stores, and an increase in the importance of independent meat wholesalers. This sector will become increasingly competitive as meat packers and processors assume additional wholesaling functions.

Except for products where freshness is a significant factor, it seems likely that most meat processing will be done by specialized meat packers and processors. In response to the demands of retail buyers, more of these products will be prepared on a custom basis and packed under the retailer's brand or label. Packers should consider a system of contracts with individual producers or with marketing agencies as a means of obtaining needed supplies of livestock. Some minimum price might be written into the contract, but the basic pricing mechanism could be tied to the wholesale meat price with appropriate adjustments for processing and handling costs.

Local auction markets have become increasingly more important in all areas between 1930 and 1959. Terminal markets have become less and less important, particularly for hogs.

There will be intense competition among markets between 1959 and 1975. As direct marketing continues to grow in importance, auction and terminal markets will handle fewer numbers of livestock. The needed bargaining power and market service demanded by buyers and sellers alike will be factors favoring the development and growth of fewer but larger markets. The potential advantage of producer cooperative marketing organizations therefore seems to be high. To be effective these organizations would need some control over the kind, quality, and timing of the livestock produced. In return, the marketing organizations would provide assistance to the producer in the form of credit and management help, and above all assure the producer of a good market for his product.

Producers will be under increasing competitive pressure between 1959 and 1975. The difference between average costs of production and lower costs achieved by more efficient operations will encourage greater production by what might be considered nonfarm firms (e.g., feed companies). As a higher and higher percentage of the fed livestock comes from the lower cost commercial units, livestock prices can be expected to move downward. This will put a further squeeze on the small livestock producers, who will have to increase production and improve efficiency if their incomes are to be maintained. Many livestock producers will find it desirable and prudent to enter into contracts covering production and marketing of livestock. In addition to services rendered under the contract, such as financing and management help, and assistance in getting breeding stock, the organization controlling a relatively large volume of livestock would be in a position to do a better job of marketing for individual producers.

While numerous changes in concentration have taken place, the increased concentration occurring in food retailing is particularly significant. There will continue to be changes in the relative bargaining power of the various components of the industry. The ability of a single firm, groups of firms, or segment of the industry arbitrarily to set prices as a monopolist seems remote. No single enterprise in the meat economy at present seems able to control supply completely. The relative ease of entry into all levels of the meat economy will continue and will make the control over supply impossible. Government intervention also tends to prevent monopoly. It should be noted, however, that it takes time for new firms to enter the industry and for the government to move in with supervision and regulation.

The food retailing segment of the meat economy will come under increasingly close scrutiny of government regulatory agencies as concentration and market influence in food retailing continue to increase. Likewise, producer groups and others can expect to come under increasingly close surveillance as they increase their power position in the industry.

Instability of livestock production creates problems throughout the entire meat economy. The longer term cycles in the production of cattle and hogs and the shorter term seasonal variation in the numbers of livestock within the year bring movements in livestock prices in the opposite direction. The longer term cycles result from imperfect price forecasting by producers, and the seasonal variations are more closely associated with the bunching of animal births. A more widespread use of contracts or an increase in vertical integration might even out short-run fluctuations but may perhaps make the longer run fluctuations even greater.

There is and will continue to be a great need for better qualified and better trained personnel at all levels of the meat economy. The competitiveness of the industry in the future will put a premium on management and research personnel. Research will have to be undertaken not only with respect to technology, but with respect to variations in the business aspects of the economy (e.g., remodeled pricing mechanisms, workable and equitable contracts).

The basic problem of agricultural adjustment—the expansion of supply faster than the expansion of demand—is not likely to be overcome by changes in concentration or vertical integration in agriculture. Devices and methods other than these will have to be employed. While the changes occurring and likely to occur in the meat economy will solve some problems, they will also create new or intensified problem areas.

(Harvard Business School, Division of Research, Soldiers Field, Boston 63, Mass.   xix + 204 pages. $3.00.   1960)

Chapter IV

FURTHER ADJUSTMENTS IN MEAT WHOLESALING

PRONOUNCED CHANGES have occurred in the wholesaling of meat products. These changes in part reflect the changing needs of the retailer that have led to his using buying specifications. Improvements in transportation, refrigeration, and other technological developments have also been responsible for changes in meat wholesaling. In recent years, there has been a relative increase in the amount of meat products moving directly from slaughtering and processing plants [1] to retail warehouses or retail stores; a relative decline in the branch house operations of the large national packers; [2] and an increase in the number and relative importance of independent meat wholesalers.

Direct Sale of Meat

The rapid growth of large-scale retail operations brought with it the need for large shipments of meat and meat products to individual retailers. Since many of these products were handled in carload lots, there was little apparent reason for channeling the meat through a branch house rather than delivering it directly to the retailer. Many of the larger retailers acquired

[1] Slaughtering refers to killing the animals and shipping meat either in wholesale or retail cuts, in fresh or frozen form. Processing includes a variety of functions such as curing, smoking, drying, grinding, canning, and the manufacture of such products as sausage and luncheon meats. Slaughtering plants may also do processing, and processing plants may do slaughtering.

[2] Packer branch houses are nonslaughtering, handling, processing, and sales establishments of packers.

meat warehouses, and some of the functions formerly performed by the packer branch house were assumed by the retailer or by decentralized packers. Other retailers have utilized the vast car route systems of the large national packers in order to obtain deliveries of meat directly to the stores. The growth and development since the 1940's of smaller independent meat packers and processors without branch house facilities also increased the relative importance of direct shipments.

During the period 1929–1948 sales of meat by packers and processors increased rapidly while combined sales by meat wholesalers and packer branch houses declined. During the period 1948–1954 the proportion of the meat moving direct to retailers from the packing plants must have declined, for the combined sales of packer branch houses and meat wholesalers increased more than twice as much as total meat production (Table 12). Although their direct sales to retailers declined between 1948 and 1954, direct sales, nevertheless, have retained a dominant position among wholesale channels of distribution.[3]

The Decline of the Branch House

In the period 1929–1948 the number of packinghouse branches fell 35% and the price-adjusted business volumes of these establishments dropped 38% (Table 12). In the period 1948–1954, aggregate business volumes of packinghouse branches increased about in proportion with the growth in volume of total meat production, while the number of branch houses continued to decline. The rate of decline in numbers of branch houses was less in the period 1948–1954 than in earlier periods.

The changes in numbers and sales volumes of branch houses until 1948 can be attributed for the most part to the shift to the direct sale of meat and meat products to retail

[3] Willard F. Williams, "Structural Changes in the Meat Industry," *Journal of Farm Economics*, Vol. XL, No. 2, May 1958, p. 324.

Table 12. Numbers of Establishments and Sales, Adjusted for Changes in Meat Prices, of Packer Branch Houses and Independent Meat Wholesale Distributors * Compared with Meat Production, Specific Years 1929–1954 and Percentage Changes for Specific Periods: 1929–1954

Year or Period of Years	Packer Branch Houses		Meat Wholesalers		Packer Branch Houses and Wholesalers		Meat Production
	Establishments	Sales †	Establishments	Sales †	Establishments	Sales †	
	Number	$1,000	Number	$1,000	Number	$1,000	Million Pounds
1954	664	2,697,483	4,357	2,866,193	5,021	5,563,676	25,333
1948	756	2,331,542	3,200	1,640,718	3,956	3,972,260	21,300
1939	940	2,893,398	2,552	1,378,231	3,492	4,271,629	17,534
1929	1,157	3,727,157	2,225	1,337,164	3,382	5,064,321	16,147
				Percentage Change			
1929–1939	−18.8	−22.4	+14.7	+3.1	+3.3	−15.7	+8.6
1929–1948	−34.7	−37.4	+43.8	+22.7	+17.0	−21.6	+31.9
1929–1954	−42.6	−27.6	+95.8	+114.3	+48.5	+9.9	+56.9
1939–1948	−19.6	−19.4	+25.4	+19.0	+13.3	−7.0	+21.5
1939–1954	−29.4	−6.8	+70.7	+108.0	+43.8	+30.2	+44.5
1948–1954	−12.2	+15.7	+36.2	+74.7	+26.9	+40.1	+18.9

* These figures do not include grocery wholesalers who handle meat.
† All sales reflect 1954 price levels since they were adjusted by the index of wholesale prices of meat and meat products, 1947–1949 = 100, adjusted such that 1954 = 100.
Source: Williams, "Economic Effects," p. 26.

organizations and the geographic decentralization of the meat packing industry. From 1948 to 1954 the change was chiefly a consolidation of branch house units into larger units with greater sales territory and volume of business per branch house unit. Estimates from trade sources indicated that the number of packer branch houses continued to decline between 1954 and 1959 but the volume of business handled by each branch house had increased.

The Growth of Independent Meat Wholesalers

Marked growth in the numbers of wholesale meat distributors and in the volume of their business has resulted in a striking change in the structure and organization of the wholesale meat industry. Between 1929 and 1954, the number of wholesalers increased from less than 2,300 to more than 4,300 (Table 12). Business volumes of meat wholesalers, as measured by sales adjusted for changes in average wholesale prices of meat, rose 108% in the period 1939–1954, whereas meat production in the United States increased only 45% in the same period. Wholesalers have therefore been handling an increasing percentage of the meat produced for slaughter.

Wholesale distributors of meat differ greatly in terms of functions performed, services rendered, species handled, size, and other characteristics. Several different types of meat wholesalers are distinguishable, but there appears to be no general agreement across the nation regarding names or titles applied to the different types or classes. The types usually identified are: [4]

1. Hotel, restaurant, and institutional supply house, referred to variously as the "H.R.I. Trade," "purveyors," and "jobbers." As implied, these wholesalers specialize in the distribution of meat to eating or dining establishments. This is the oldest type.

[4] Williams, "Economic Effects," pp. 28–29.

2. Meat wholesalers selling mainly to retailers, both chain and independent, and to jobbers. These are relatively large volume firms, fewer in number and larger in size than the jobbers. A few firms concentrate on the distribution of dressed calves or pork, but most specialize in beef—in the purchase of beef carcasses from packers, and in the sale of wholesale beef cuts. Consequently, they are often referred to as "beef breakers" [5] or "breakers."

3. "Boners" are wholesalers principally engaged in removing bones and sinews from lower grade carcasses and in selling the meat to processing plants and retailers. Like the breakers, boners are almost exclusively concerned with beef. Boners as well as breakers emerged during World War II as separate and distinct from the packers. The sales volume of the boners is on the average smaller than the breakers', but the volume of beef handled by the boners is large.

4. Frozen meat handlers specializing in such products as chip steaks, veal patties, quick frozen cuts, and other frozen meat products. These wholesalers usually sell the bulk of their meat direct to retail stores, but they may also supply jobbers.

5. Local wholesalers such as the sausage processors and the producers of other specialty products.

Many packers, particularly the national packers, continue to do their own breaking and boning. Direct sales to restaurants and other dining establishments are important to a few packers, but to an increasing extent these functions have been shifted to specialists—the meat wholesalers. While many retail stores buy most of their meat directly from the meat packers or processors, these retailers find it advantageous to obtain a part of their needs from specialized wholesalers. Specialized wholesalers provide specific cuts of meat not regularly obtainable from packers or processors. In addition, the specialized wholesaler might also be used as a source of supply when the

[5] The term breaking means cutting or dividing carcasses into quarters and wholesale cuts, i.e., ribs, loins, chucks, rounds, etc.

retailer must meet his needs immediately since the wholesaler may be closer than the packer.

There is evidence that meat wholesalers have become somewhat more important than packer branch houses in areas of the country where population growth and the consequent retail store growth have been rapid.[6] Meat packers and processors may be reluctant to construct new branch house operations in these areas because of the recent trend toward the closing or consolidation of branch houses in other areas. The growth of independent, specialized slaughterers also has contributed to the growth in the numbers of meat wholesalers. These independent slaughterers often rely upon independent wholesalers for distribution of their products.[7]

Future Developments in Meat Wholesaling

Future developments in the wholesaling of meat depend on the answers to three important questions. Who will perform the functions thought of as wholesaling? The retail grocer in his own warehouse, the grocery wholesaler, or the specialized meat wholesaler? Will the hotel, restaurant, and institutional market expand more than the home consumption market? We have already discussed the answer to these two questions. The third question is, whether the specialized wholesalers will continue to gain in importance compared with meat packers and processors. Or will the meat packers and processors increasingly take over the wholesaling function? What role will the branch house then play? These questions must be answered for a projection of the future of meat wholesaling.

[6] See Appendix Table 12 for a regional breakdown of changes in the sale of packinghouse branches and independent wholesale distributors.
[7] Williams, "Structural Changes," p. 328.

Changes in Meat Retailing

The projected changes in meat retailing indicate that an increasing percentage of the total meat supply will be purchased by retail organizations with warehouse facilities. With existing technology this means that a greater number of the wholesaling functions for beef, veal, or lamb (breaking, boning, etc.) are likely to be performed by the retailer either in the warehouse or in the store.

As the retailing units increase in volume, the need for auxiliary meat supplies may decrease. Larger retail organizations may be able to program their needs somewhat more closely and make needed short run supply adjustments internally.

Branch house sales have been chiefly to independent retailers and meat markets. If this continues, the decline in the number of small independent stores will tend to reduce the need for branch house operations further. On the other hand, the possibility of expansion in numbers of superettes will open new sales outlets for branch houses and specialized wholesalers. The continued decentralization of the meat packing and processing industry, particularly into new geographic areas of the country, also tends to reduce the need for branch house operations in these areas. Continued improvements in refrigeration and transportation also make the branch house less essential in meat distribution. On balance, it seems that unless branch houses cater to the needs of larger retailers or to the hotel, restaurant, and institutional market, they will become less important in the wholesaling of meat and meat products.

Expansion of the Hotel, Restaurant, and Institutional Market

Even though the on-premise consumption of meat represented by the hotel, restaurant, and institutional market may be smaller than commonly thought, it represents a sizable outlet for meat and meat products. Projections for the future indicate that this market is likely to become more important both in terms of the percentage of total pounds of meat consumed and in terms of the percentage of total expenditures of consumers for food. The relatively high elasticity of demand for services in this market should be of particular interest to those agencies serving the market—meat packers and processors and specialized wholesalers.

The hotel, restaurant, and institutional market of the future will demand (1) larger quantities of product both in total and as a percentage of the total meat supply and (2) considerably more services such as portion-controlled cuts of meat. In some instances these cuts may be partially or wholly cooked and otherwise prepared for serving. The increasingly specialized nature of this outlet for meat tends to give the local wholesaler an advantage over meat packers and processors located some distance from the market. In addition the local wholesaler often gives more personalized services than the large national packers and their branch houses.

It is apparent, however, that the hotel, restaurant, and institutional market is becoming increasingly attractive to meat packers. Efforts of meat packers to capture an increasing share of this market are likely to take two different forms. First, current branch house operations are likely to be altered so that the branch house closely resembles an independent meat wholesaler. Initially this will mean that more cutting and processing will be carried on there. Ultimately, as technology changes, the cutting and processing may be shifted to more central locations. Meat packers and processors will also energetically attempt to service the hotel, restaurant, and institutional trade in geographic areas surrounding present or future locations of meat packing and processing facilities.

In addition to the expansion of services from present facilities, meat packers and processors may attempt to establish close ties with existing independent meat wholesalers. For the most part, this would mean a merger or the purchase of the wholesaler by the packer. A type of captive firm relationship through formal or informal contracts could also be established with independent meat wholesalers. Since purchases and mergers would give meat packers and processors greater assurance of control over the wholesale business, they will be more important than formal or informal contracts.

The rapid expansion of independent meat wholesalers since World War II has included many relatively inefficient small firms. Faced with increasing competition, not only from other wholesale meat distributors, but also from meat packers and processors, it seems likely that the number of independent meat wholesalers may stabilize or even decline. The volume of business of independent meat wholesalers will continue to expand as the hotel, restaurant, and institutional market expands. On the other hand, the rate of increase in the share of the market claimed by independent meat wholesalers is likely to slow down in response to increased competition from meat packers and processors for both the retail and the hotel, restaurant, and institutional market. Thus, until approximately 1965 the relative volume of business of the meat wholesalers will continue to grow but at a decreasing rate each year. From 1965 to 1975 the increased competition with packers and processors will probably stabilize or cause a decline in the proportion of sales of meat through independent meat wholesalers.

Chapter V

MEAT PACKERS AND PROCESSORS

THE MEAT packing and processing segment of the meat economy has been cited often as an industry with a relatively high
degree of concentration. Early in the history of the industry, a
few large firms handled a high percentage of the total output.
Over the years there have been changes in the composition of
the large firms as well as in the degree of concentration in the
industry. In general, the concentration of the industry as measured by the percentage of total output handled by a few large
firms has moved downward because new firms have entered the
industry and existing smaller firms have grown larger.

Interest is focused upon concentration in an industry in order to help gauge either the exercise of, or ability to exercise,
bargaining power or market influence. While it cannot be
measured statistically, it seems that the bargaining power or
market influence of the meat packing and processing industry
has gradually declined. Perhaps the three most important factors back of this change have been (1) internal changes within
the meat packing and processing industry itself, such as the
entry of new firms and the decentralization and specialization
of meat packing and processing, (2) changes in the market
structure of food retailing and wholesaling, and the market
for meat, and (3) changes in relative bargaining power of producers or producer groups as production units and marketing
organizations increased in size, market news was improved, and
more market outlets became available to producers.

Reduced Concentration

The percentage of the commercial slaughter of cattle accounted for by the four leading firms dropped steadily from about 54% in 1916 to about 31% in 1955 (Table 13). Although concentration in calf slaughter increased steadily until about 1929, it too declined between that time and 1955. The

Table 13. Percentages of Total Commercial Slaughter Accounted for by the Four Leading Meat Packers by Species, Selected Years, 1916 to 1955

	Percentages of Total Commercial Slaughter Accounted for by Four Leading Firms			
Year	*Cattle*	*Calves*	*Sheep and Lambs*	*Hogs*
1955	30.8%	34.7%	58.5%	36.4%
1947	38.3	39.6	67.8	40.4
1935	46.6	46.3	70.5	41.4
1929	49.9	46.9	70.7	40.2
1924	50.5	40.1	66.4	44.7
1916 *	53.9	32.1	70.2	51.2

* Includes Morris and Co., acquired by Armour and Company in 1923.
Source: Williams, "Economic Effects," p. 21.

concentration of sheep and lamb slaughter has increased and decreased a number of times between 1916 and 1955, when it had declined well below its 1916 level. Concentration in hog slaughter declined greatly after World War I and has continued to decrease almost continuously. In total, between 1935 and 1955 the four leading firms have accounted for a steadily decreasing percentage of industry slaughter of each of the species.

In 1954 the four largest companies in the meat packing industry accounted for 39% of the value of shipments of all packers (Table 14). The level of concentration among the four leading firms in terms of value of shipments in 1954 was lowest for fresh beef, averaging 36% of the total value of shipments. The concentration by the four largest firms was highest for lamb and mutton and "other meat packing products"—mostly sausage and other prepared meats. The firms

Table 14. Concentration Ratios of Employment and Value of Shipments and Slaughter in the Meat Packing Industry, for Various Product Classes, 1954

	Concentration Ratios in Terms of Volume of —				
	4 Largest Companies	4 5th–8th Largest	8 Largest Companies	12 9th–20th Largest	20 Largest Companies
Meat Packing, Entire Industry					
Value of Shipments	39%	12%	51%	9%	60%
Employment	44	12	56	9	65
Meat Packing Product Classes					
Value of Shipments:					
Fresh beef	36	7	43	8	51
Fresh veal	49	7	56	11	67
Fresh lamb and mutton	61	13	74	13	87
Fresh pork	42	14	56	13	69
Lard	45	18	63	15	78
Hides, skins, and pelts	43	6	49	8	57
Other meat packing products	61	8	69	10	79

Source: *Concentration in American Industry*, Report of the Subcommittee on Antitrust and Monopoly to the Committee on the Judiciary, U. S. Senate (Washington, Government Printing Office, 1957), pp. 63, 69, 220, 382.

ranking fifth through eighth in size accounted for only 7% of total industry shipments of beef. These four firms, as well as the twelve that were ninth through twentieth largest, tended to concentrate on pork. The twenty largest packers accounted for 87% of the value of the lamb and mutton shipments but only 51% of the shipments of fresh beef. In total, the twenty largest companies accounted for 60% of the value of shipments in the meat packing industry in 1954.

During the 1947–1955 period the four leading firms lost ground rather steadily in the proportion of total slaughter of beef and lamb but no marked trends in hog and veal slaughter are evident.[1] The percentage of commercial slaughter accounted for by each of the four leading firms either dropped during 1947–1955 or remained relatively constant. In 1955 one of these firms ceased slaughtering at a number of locations and since 1955 another closed several slaughtering plants. Accordingly data for 1947–1957 would show more marked downtrends in the percentage of commercial slaughter by the four leading firms than was indicated in the 1947–1955 period. On the other hand, concentration among firms ranking fifth to tenth largest tended to increase slightly during the period from 1947 to 1955 primarily as a result of their increasing emphasis on hogs and processed meat products.[2]

The trend in the concentration ratios in the meat packing industry has resulted from the interaction of many forces. A downtrend in concentration of hog, sheep, and lamb slaughtering began with the growth of small independent packers during and immediately after World War I. The downward movement in concentration in the industry occurring since World War II, particularly for beef and lamb and mutton, can be explained by the relatively greater increase in the numbers of large independent meat packers and processors and in the increase in the volume of their business compared with the national packers.

Growth of Independent Plants

During the period 1950–1955 the number of large nonfederally inspected plants increased about 31%. In the same period, the number of federally inspected plants (which includes

[1] See Appendix Table 13 for annual data for 1947–1955 on share of slaughter of various species handled by the four largest and ten largest meat packing companies.

[2] Williams, "Economic Effects," p. 22.

almost all the plants of the large national packers as well as many independently operated plants) increased only 3%. The number of small nonfederally inspected plants dropped substantially during the 1950–1955 period (Table 15). About the

Table 15. Number of Meat Packers by Type and Percentage Changes, 1950 and 1955

| | Meat Packing Plants | | |
Type of Packer	1950	1955	Percentage Change 1950–55
	Number	Number	Per Cent
Federally Inspected	441	455	+3.2
Large Nonfederally Inspected *	725	952	+31.3
Small Nonfederally Inspected †	2,072	1,810	−12.6
Total	3,238	3,217	−0.6

* Includes nonfederally inspected plants slaughtering over 2 million pounds liveweight annually. This classification is referred to as "other wholesale" in USDA reports.

† Includes nonfederally inspected plants slaughtering less than 2 million pounds liveweight annually but more than 300,000 pounds. This classification is referred to as "local" in USDA reports.

Source: U. S. Agricultural Marketing Service, *Number of Livestock Slaughtering Establishments March 1, 1950, and March 1, 1955* (Washington, Government Printing Office, 1954 and 1959).

same percentage of the total meat supply was handled by federally inspected plants in 1955 as in 1950. Any declines in the concentration ratios must therefore have come about through a greater relative growth in the volume of business of the independent federally inspected slaughterers. Large nonfederally inspected plants increased in number and in volume of business between 1950 and 1955. Increases in numbers of this kind of plant resulted largely from the growth in volume of small nonfederally inspected plants that qualified as large instead of small plants.

The basic change during the period 1947–1955 was an increase in the number of independent packers handling beef and lamb and mutton at faster rates than increases experienced by the large national packers handling the same commodities. During the same period, there was an increase in the percentage of the total supply of pork handled by the large national packers, especially those ranking fifth to tenth in size.

In general, the plants of the independent meat packers and processors handled only one or two species of livestock while the large national packers generally handled several.

Reasons for Growth of Independent Plants

The rise in the importance of the independent federally inspected and the large nonfederally inspected meat packers as compared with large national packers can be attributed to several factors. Among these are differences in the cost structure of the two types of organizations, in the kind and type of service rendered retailers and wholesalers, and in the use of federal grades in merchandising beef and lamb.

Cost Differences. Trade representatives of both large and small packing companies implied that in the past the larger national packers held a "cost umbrella" over many of the small operators.[3] The large packers quite often had old facilities with supposed inefficiency and high costs. In addition, the bigger operators had higher overhead expenses and higher advertising and promotion expenditures associated with the development of packer labels on their products. The smaller plants were often of more recent construction and hence could be expected to include more of the new cost-saving devices. These smaller plants usually had low overhead and selling expense also. There is little comparable cost data available to bear out these opinions. Perhaps the best evidence is the loss in the

[3] Impressions gained from interviews with trade representatives.

share of the market handled by the larger packers and the growth of relatively small packing operations, although even here factors other than relative costs are operative.

Differences in Service. Some retailer representatives interviewed maintained that they received better service from smaller packers than from larger packers. The retailers felt that shipments from large national packers were likely to be less uniform either in quality, conformation, or weight than comparable shipments from smaller, more specialized meat packers. This was true regardless of whether the meat was purchased on the basis of packer or U. S. grades.

Other retailers expressed the opinion that some of the large national packers hewed close to the line on quality so that the shipment was just good enough to keep the retail buyer from returning the shipment. This necessitates the checking of nearly every load by the retail buyer to be sure that it is acceptable. Such lack of confidence in suppliers also held back the shipment of meat to stores without its first being inspected at a central warehouse.

Another point mentioned was the fact that the sales forces of the major packers are so organized that they are more difficult to deal with than sales people representing the smaller operations. For example, a retail meat buyer for a small chain or an independent operator may wish to buy more than one meat product. He must, therefore, deal with more than one of the salesmen of the national packers. Salesmen for smaller packers can and usually do sell a variety of products. In addition, the representatives of the smaller packing firms are in a position in their company where they can more readily make decisions regarding price and other adjustments than the representatives of the larger packers. Retailers also point out that smaller packers are often more realistic in their prices than the larger packers. These retail representatives say they have been forced into relatively expensive buying operations because they could not "trust" their suppliers to give them the same price that was being given to their competitors for comparable quality and service. Therefore, the retailers have to check quotations from a number of sources and haggle with packers over prices as well as check the quality of the meat.

All these retailer complaints about the services rendered by the major packers seem to be about situations that could be corrected easily. On the other hand, if their complaints are unfounded, the problem becomes one for the packers' public relations department. Although the retailer made a few of these same complaints about smaller meat packers and processors also, their complaints regarding small packers were limited almost wholly to lack of volume, incomplete line of product, and unstable financial position.

Use of Federal Grades. To an increasing extent beef and lamb were sold on a federal grade basis during the 1947–1955 period. The increased use of federal grades for beef provided a means by which smaller packers could better compete with the national packers. Government grades put a seal of quality on the beef, which previously had been provided only by the grades of the national packers.[4] Retail buyers in general approved of federal grades on beef and lamb and began to buy and merchandise these meats on the basis of federal grades. The national packers resisted the shift away from packer grades to U. S. grades on fresh meat. This resistance was apparently based upon a feeling that packer grades were more equitable and provided for more efficient pricing than federal grades. In addition, the national packers had a considerable investment in the packer brands, which they wanted to protect if at all possible. Independent meat packers and processors, on the other hand, were eager to sell beef and lamb on the basis of U. S. grades. This difference in attitude between the national

[4] For a more complete discussion of this subject, see Williams, "Economic Effects," p. 56.

packers and the independent packers may help explain the relative growth of the independent packers during the early 1950's.

Geographic Decentralization. Between 1950 and 1955 there were an increasing number of all three types of packing plants in the South, and a decrease in the number of small, noninspected plants and an increase in the number of larger, noninspected plants in all other regions. In regions other than the South, small noninspected plants either went out of business or increased their sales volumes to become larger plants. Despite a sharp increase in numbers of larger noninspected plants in the Northeast a considerable number of the small plants in this region ceased operations and the total number of plants in this area dropped 18% during the period 1950–1955.[5]

These data indicate in part the geographical decentralization that has been taking place in the meat packing and processing industry, particularly the relative growth of the industry in the South. Within the various geographical areas there has been a decentralization under way as slaughter volumes at Chicago, San Francisco, eastern slaughtering centers, and other large metropolitan centers have dropped. Livestock slaughter in outlying areas has increased. Freight differentials between meat and live animals are usually given as the reason for the general move of packing plants closer to the areas of livestock supply. Wage rate differentials, obsolescence of old plants and equipment, and population movements have also played a role in the decentralization of the industry.

Two major changes in the structure of the meat packing industry have resulted in the decentralization: (1) the closing of plants in Chicago and other slaughtering centers by the national packers and the consequent shift of slaughtering and processing to established or new plants in other areas and

---

[5] See Appendix Table 14 for a regional breakdown of number and volume of different types of plants.

(2) the growth of the independent slaughterers or processors both in terms of numbers and volume of sales.

Competition in the Meat Packing Industry

The national packers seem locked in a very intensive competitive struggle with the operators of smaller independent plants, particularly in the slaughtering and selling of beef and lamb. The bigger operators often lay their troubles to the advent of the widespread use of federal grades. There can be little question that federal grades on beef have made it easier for the smaller operator located some distance from the market to sell his product. In addition to the advantages offered by federal grading, many of the smaller firms have relatively less overhead expense and often owners and others work extra hours without overtime pay.

On the other hand, the larger organizations have various advantages over smaller firms: for example, availability of larger shipments; a more complete line of products; and specialized sales, advertising, and merchandising personnel. The larger meat packing firms have made many changes designed to reduce costs and increase net profit and return on investment. Since the results of these changes have been encouraging, even more changes are in the offing.

In spite of the adjustments made or to be made, the larger meat packers may find it difficult to match the costs per unit of the smaller so-called "cinder block" operators, especially in beef slaughter. In addition, the return on capital invested in such slaughtering operations by the large packers may be lower than alternative uses for capital invested elsewhere. Should this be the case, the larger meat packers may tend to de-emphasize fresh beef operations in favor of processed meats, other food, or nonfood products. The market for these processed products will be expanding and more effective use of brands can therefore be made on them.

This does not mean that the large meat packer will move out of the fresh meat business. The change will be a shift in emphasis since fresh meat will necessarily be carried as a service to buyers. Not all of the major packers will make this change in product emphasis. If one or a few large firms do shift their emphasis to processed meats or other products, all firms may benefit. The firms that do not change will then have an opportunity for greater volume of fresh meat sales as they take over the sales volume of the firm or firms de-emphasizing fresh meat. Widespread use of frozen meat would again give the larger national packer a competitive advantage in meat sales. The product would then be similar to a processed product, and could be differentiated in the eyes of the consumer by the use of brand names.

Federal grading of beef seems to be firmly entrenched in the retail trade, accepted by consumers, and at least in part sanctioned by producers. It seems highly probable therefore that the government grading system, at least on beef, is here to stay. Whether grading on pork is desirable or not is debatable. Many well-qualified persons within the industry support each view. For those who want to avoid grading, a lesson may be gained from the experience with beef. The industry may have to produce a higher quality, more uniform product than is currently available if grading on pork is to be avoided.

Many of the representatives of the meat packing and processing industry feel that the return on capital invested in this industry is too low compared with other industries. An analysis of the meat packing industry for investors indicated that the managements of major meat packing companies have been taking several paths to improve their profit position. First and most important has been a reshaping of facilities devoted to meat production in order to modernize these operations and accommodate them to the changing character of meat marketing as fully as possible. Obsolete slaughtering plants and branch houses have been abandoned and new regional proc-

essing and warehousing facilities are being developed.[6] Many
firms are also seeking more aggressive management to deal
with current problems.

In speaking with us the officials of the national packers emphasized that they all have been improving their operations.
Overhead expenses have been cut, processing and slaughtering
operations have been decentralized, many branch houses have
been closed or consolidated, and new merchandising methods have been adopted. Some of the new slaughtering plants
built by national packers are smaller, more flexible plants than
the facilities that were closed. Thus, instead of a few large
plants, many national packers now have several smaller plants
scattered over a wider geographical area. The latter part of the
1950's was a period of rapid—almost revolutionary—change for
most of the national meat packers.

The expansion in meat production and consumption predicted for 1975 will call for a sizable upward adjustment in
slaughtering and processing facilities. Initially the need for
added facilities may be met by remodeling and expanding the
present plants. Ultimately, however, new plants in both the
older and newer livestock producing areas will be needed. Currently there is a tendency in the industry to favor the construction of somewhat smaller, more specialized plants. Reaction
against the relatively old, large, and comparable inefficient
plant with which the industry has been saddled should not be
allowed to obscure economies of scale that may still be present in the industry.

Changes in Procurement of Livestock

The competitive situation within the meat packing and
processing industry and between meat packers and retailers
and wholesalers will probably enable retail and wholesale buyers to obtain the kinds and quantities of product and the type

---

[6] Elliot Schneider, *The Meat Packing Industry* (New York, Paine, Webber,
Jackson & Curtis), July 1958, p. 7.

of service they want. The relative bargaining power of the two groups will determine whether any added costs will be borne by the meat packer and processor or the buyer or shared by both groups.

The market situation shaping up in the future raises serious questions as to the adequacy of the present system of marketing livestock. The variation in total supply of livestock, both in quantity and quality, coming to the existing dealer yards, auctions, terminal markets, and other collecting points makes it extremely difficult for meat packers and processors to match the available supply of livestock to the demand for meat efficiently. Perhaps a new system of production and marketing of livestock is needed.

If meat packers and processors are not alert to the changing market needs and do not make appropriate changes, others in the meat economy may step in to bridge the gap. Retailers and other buyers, for example, may establish closer working relations with producers or producer groups, or vice versa. The livestock might be slaughtered and processed on a custom basis or in plants owned by either the buyer or the producer. Operations of this type are increasing in number, especially in the production and marketing of hogs. Aggressive action by meat packers and processors may not halt forward or backward integration of livestock producers, marketing agencies, and retail buyers. A number of choices are open to meat packers and processors that would help protect their market position by minimizing the type of integration just outlined.

Use of Contracts. To help cope with this situation, packers and processors should consider the use of contracts or informal arrangements with livestock marketing organizations, large producers, and feed companies, or others controlling supplies of livestock. This would make it possible to tailor more closely the kind and type of livestock available to market needs and demands. The contracts and informal agreements could specify the kinds of animals to be fed, the type of feeding program, and the expected time of marketing.

Pricing under the contract or informal arrangement could be worked out on the basis of the wholesale price received for the product with appropriate conversion factors to a live-weight basis. This procedure is already in use in buying cattle from Western feedlots as well as at other locations. In the past, producers have apparently placed considerable impor-tance on being able to see their livestock sold. This producer desire is usually listed as one of the main factors behind the growth of auction selling. The large-scale producers of the fu-ture will have more confidence in the packers or other buyers and will be more willing to sell on a delivered basis. This as-sumes, of course, that the buyers will offer the kind of contract and act on a basis that promotes such confidence on the part of the producer.

Production and marketing contracts will grow in relative im-portance between 1959 and 1975 as a means of procurement of livestock supplies by meat packers. Initially, the production and marketing contracts will be applied to hogs. Later more beef feeding will also be done under some kind of contractual arrangement. The other party to the contract in addition to the meat packer may be (1) a producer, (2) a marketing or-ganization—either cooperative or independent, or (3) a feed company or other group controlling supplies of livestock.

There are many factors inherent in the production and mar-keting of livestock which will play a part in the decision as to which of the above three groups will likely be the major con-tracting party. Meat packers may have relatively little control or influence over these inherent factors in the production and marketing of livestock. As one of the contracting parties, how-ever, meat packers can exercise a great deal of influence in the decision as to who the other contracting party is likely to be. The terms of the contract and the relative emphasis placed on contracts with the different groups will certainly help decide which group will be the other party to the contract covering livestock production and marketing.

Livestock Feeding by Meat Packers. Reports filed by meat packers under the Packers and Stockyards Act [7] indicate that in 1957 there were 143 meat packers in the cattle feeding business.[8] These packers fed 518,742 head of cattle in 1957. In 1954, 486,126 head of cattle were fed by 160 packers. This was about 5% of all cattle fed. Packers feed for delivery of fat cattle during times of relatively light supplies of fat cattle. Executives of packing companies indicate that feeding cattle in their own yards, or on a custom basis, gives the packers flexibility and bargaining power and augments supplies during periods when supplies of some types are short.

Information collected from representatives of the national packers indicated that the numbers of cattle fed by these organizations since 1957 have continued fairly steady. If there was any noticeable trend in numbers fed, it was down rather than up. Feeding in the packers' own yards seems to be decreasing and feeding on a custom basis increasing. In California, meat packers feel that it is necessary to feed on contract for finished cattle for a fairly high percentage of their total supply for slaughtering. Kramer reports that California packers told him that they found it necessary to supply one-third to two-thirds of their total kill from their own feedlots or through contracts with feedlots.[9] Apparently this is not the case in other sections of the country.

The ten largest packers reported that they did not have any hogs on feed during the 1954–1957 period. In total, packers reported that 8,431 hogs were fed during 1957. This compared

[7] This act was passed by the United States Congress in 1921. The primary purpose of the act is to assure fair competition and fair trade practices in livestock marketing and in the meat packing industry.

[8] See Appendix Table 15 for number of packing firms feeding livestock 1954 to 1957.

[9] R. C. Kramer, "Cattle Feeding," p. 10.

with 11,921 hogs in 1956. During the 1954–1957 period, the number of firms reporting hog feeding operations varied between 20 and 31.[10] The number of hogs fed by packers is an almost infinitesimal part of the total hog supply. In recent years several packers have been experimenting with producing hogs under various types of contract arrangements, but as of 1959, the number of hogs produced for packers under contract was still very small.

More livestock feeding by packers would in a sense fulfill the same purposes as production under contract—control over the quality and timing of sale. Feeding by meat packers would probably require a greater investment by packers per unit of production than would a system of contract production and marketing. It seems probable that contracts will be emphasized and that livestock fed by meat packers in their own feedlots will continue to supply only a small part of their needs.

Changes in the Bargaining Power of Livestock Producers

The typical producer of livestock supplies so small a share of the total market that his individual actions have little or no appreciable effect on the general level of the prices of the product he sells. Yet individual producers can and do have some influence over the prices they receive in relation to the general level of prices existing at any one time. Certainly the management decisions such as what, when, where, and how to produce and sell the product will influence the price and returns received by livestock producers.[11] Bargaining power and marketing skill achieved either as individuals or through a producer marketing organization may increase prices and returns. How much control the individual producer has over

[10] U. S. Agricultural Marketing Service, Packers and Stockyards Docket #16, "Feeding Operations of Meat Packers" (Washington, Government Printing Office, September 1958), p. 7.

[11] See Appendix Tables 16 and 17 for percentages of cattle and hogs sold by farmers through various types of outlets.

prices and returns, particularly in the short-run marketing situation, is debatable. Recently opportunities have arisen for producers to increase their control over prices. These developments include the growth in size of the production unit, growth of producer marketing organizations, changes in marketing channels and marketing agencies, increased and improved market news and outlook information, and improved transportation and communications facilities.

At the same time, changes have occurred in the production and marketing of livestock and meat that have tended to reduce the relative market influence of livestock producers. Some of the changes in food retailing and wholesaling have had this effect. On balance, the net effect of past developments seems to have been a strengthening of producer market influence, particularly in relation to meat packers and processors. Some of the past and future changes in the production and marketing of livestock will be discussed in the following chapters of this report.

Chapter VI

SHIFTS IN THE MARKETING OF LIVESTOCK

SIGNIFICANT CHANGES have taken place in the marketing channels through which livestock moves from the producer to the meat packer or processor, as well as in the marketing agencies handling the livestock. Some of these shifts, such as increased direct buying of hogs by meat packers, resulted from the integration of the local assembly, transportation, and purchase functions with the functions of meat packing and processing. Other changes in marketing channels and agencies such as the growth of auction selling were nearly independent in nature, not related closely to the actions of agencies at other functional levels in the meat economy. Changes in transportation and communications, particularly the advent of the motor truck, radio, and telephone, have also played an important role in reshaping the channels and agencies used in marketing livestock. The decentralization of meat packing facilities away from large urban centers such as Chicago, San Francisco, and the eastern seaboard markets has also had a pronounced effect on the marketing of livestock.

There are a variety of marketing outlets open to livestock producers. One of the oldest methods of marketing livestock is direct selling, that is, the sale of livestock by the producer directly to the packer, local dealer, or other farmers. The sale is consummated without the assistance of commission men, selling agents, buying agents, or brokers. In 1955 approximately 38% of the livestock marketed by farmers was through direct sales (Table 16). Another major market outlet for livestock is the so-called central or terminal public market. At these mar-

Table 16. Livestock Sold by Farmers Through Different Market Outlets, United States, 1955

| Kind of Livestock ‡ | Number Marketed * (1,000) | Terminal Public Markets | Auctions | Type of Market Outlet | | | | | |
| | | | | Direct Selling | | | | | |
				to Packers †	to Local Dealers	to Farmers	Total	All Others	Total
All livestock ‡	61,156	34.2%	25.7%	14.7%	15.1%	8.2%	38.0%	2.1%	100.0%
Cattle	33,542	38.4	28.6	11.8	9.3	9.5	30.6	2.4	100.0
Calves under 1 year of age	18,389	21.6	43.0	7.5	14.3	10.2	32.0	3.4	100.0
Hogs and pigs	77,512	30.8	16.5	21.4	25.3	4.9	51.6	1.1	100.0
Sheep and lambs	21,105	34.7	14.1	21.1	14.9	12.0	48.0	3.2	100.0

* Estimated from the Survey of Farmers' Expenditures in 1955.
† Includes local butchers.
‡ Measured in terms of marketing equivalents—equal to 1 head of cattle, 3 calves, 4 hogs, or 10 sheep.

Source: Phillips and Engelman, "Market Outlets," p. 11.

kets livestock are assembled in large numbers to be sold primarily by an agent of the producer. Most of the larger terminal markets operating in 1958 were established in the latter half of the nineteenth century. Marketing through terminal markets accounted for 34% of all livestock sold in 1955. A third method of selling, which has gained importance in the 1950's, is the livestock auction. Livestock auctions are trading centers where animals are sold by public bidding to the buyer who offers the highest price per hundredweight or per head. Auction markets usually draw their supplies from the communities in which they are located. Approximately 25% of all livestock marketed in 1955 was through auction markets.

Changes in Marketing Channels

Prior to the establishment of the terminal markets, practically all the livestock in the country were sold by producers on a direct selling basis. With the development of the railroad and the appearance of the first terminal market in Chicago in 1865, direct selling declined in importance. From World War I to the late 1930's the proportion of livestock moving through the terminal markets decreased and direct selling became increasingly important. Since the 1930's terminal markets continued to decline in importance as sales through auction markets increased.[1]

Terminal Markets

In 1923 federally inspected slaughterers purchased 90% of their cattle in terminal markets (Figure 2). In 1951 73% of the slaughter cattle was purchased at terminal markets. In 1956, it was estimated that this figure had dropped to 70%. The drop in the proportion of hogs purchased at terminal mar-

[1] U. S. Agricultural Marketing Service, Marketing Research Report No. 216, "Market Outlets for Livestock Producers," by Victor B. Phillips and Gerald Engelman (Washington, Government Printing Office, March 1958), p. 9.

Figure 2

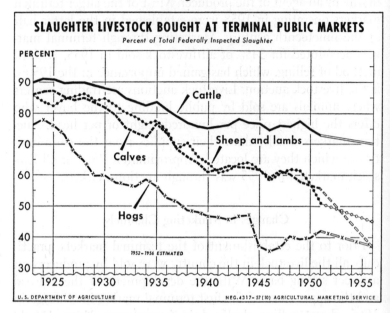

SLAUGHTER LIVESTOCK BOUGHT AT TERMINAL PUBLIC MARKETS

Percent of Total Federally Inspected Slaughter

U.S. DEPARTMENT OF AGRICULTURE   NEG.4317- 57(10) AGRICULTURAL MARKETING SERVICE

kets by federally inspected slaughterers was even more drastic
in dropping from 77% in 1923 to an estimated 37% in 1956.
The percentage of slaughter calves and sheep and lambs
bought at terminal markets also dropped substantially during
the period.

During the period 1945–1957 total receipts at public stockyards did not decline appreciably except for sheep and lambs
(Figure 3). During the years 1945–1957 an increasing percentage of the receipts at terminal markets did not move directly
to slaughter. The relative decline in receipts at terminal markets was therefore smaller than the slaughter statistics indicate.

A comparison of the percentage of total livestock that passed
through public stockyards in the years 1935–1956 indicates
that the decrease in the importance of the terminal markets
has been greater for sheep, lambs, calves, and hogs than for

Figure 3

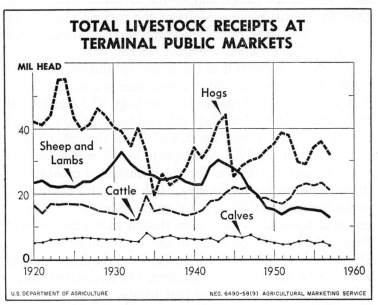

TOTAL LIVESTOCK RECEIPTS AT TERMINAL PUBLIC MARKETS

MIL HEAD

Hogs

40

Sheep and Lambs

Cattle

20

Calves

0

1920   1930   1940   1950   1960

U.S. DEPARTMENT OF AGRICULTURE   NEG. 6490-58(9) AGRICULTURAL MARKETING SERVICE

cattle.[2] In the North Central States terminals declined in importance as a market outlet for cattle, calves, and hogs from 1940 to 1956,[3] and Chicago decreased in importance more than terminal markets as a group. Over the 1947 to 1956 period there have been increases in receipts of some species, especially cattle, at Cleveland, Indianapolis, South St. Paul, and St. Louis and a few other markets.[4] In general, however, there has been a continued decline in the relative importance of terminal markets as outlets for livestock. The decline in numbers of livestock sold at the terminal markets during the 1920's was

[2] See Appendix Table 18 for more detailed information on changes in terminal market receipts.

[3] R. R. Newberg, *Livestock Marketing in the North Central Region*, Research Bulletin 846 (Wooster, Ohio, Ohio Agricultural Experiment Station, December 1959), pp. 25, 44.

[4] U. S. Agricultural Marketing Service, Statistical Bulletin No. 230, *Livestock and Meat Statistics, 1957* (Washington, Government Printing Office, July 1958), p. 50.

due primarily to the increase in the number of hard surface roads and motor trucks, and to the favorable freight rates given to internal packers. Shifts of the packing plants away from the cities with terminal stockyards also contributed to the relative decline in terminal market receipts.[5]

It seems probable that in the future terminal markets will continue to decline in relative importance as a market outlet for slaughter livestock, particularly for hogs. The changes will be gradual. Terminal markets will still be important market outlets for cattle, calves, sheep, and lambs throughout most of the period 1959–1975. Widespread use of production and marketing contracts toward the end of this period could greatly reduce terminal market receipts. Under a contract system of production and marketing, however, the animals might be received at terminal markets even though they were not sold there. Chicago will continue to decline in importance, but other terminals such as South St. Paul and the River markets will probably become more important. The receipts of the livestock commission companies that handle almost all of the livestock at the terminal markets will of course decrease. Opportunities for commission companies in the future will depend chiefly upon how well they adapt their operations to the new industry pattern.

The factors tending to reduce terminal market receipts in the future will be the continued decentralization of the meat packing and processing industry, the growth of production and marketing contracts, and the continued expansion of direct shipments of live animals, especially hogs, to slaughterers.

Auction Markets

During the 1930's the number of livestock auction markets increased rapidly (Figure 4). In the 1940's the number in-

[5] U. S. Agricultural Marketing Service, Marketing Research Report No. 299, "Livestock Terminal Markets in the United States," by Edward Uvacek and Dalton L. Wilson (Washington, Government Printing Office, January 1959), p. 2.

Figure 4

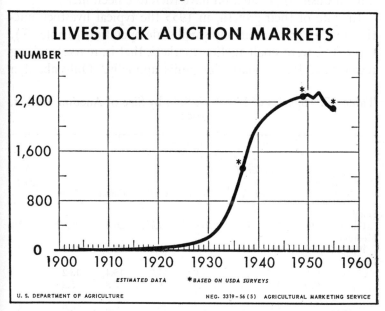

LIVESTOCK AUCTION MARKETS

NUMBER

2,400

1,600

800

0

1900   1910   1920   1930   1940   1950   1960

ESTIMATED DATA   ✱BASED ON USDA SURVEYS*

U. S. DEPARTMENT OF AGRICULTURE   NEG. 3319-56 (5)   AGRICULTURAL MARKETING SERVICE

creased more slowly. And from 1950 to 1955, the number was stable for a while and then declined. From 1940 to 1956 auction markets became increasingly important. Auction markets are much more widely scattered over the United States than the terminal markets. The geographical decentralization of auction markets makes it possible for the livestock producer to see his livestock sold under a competitive bidding process. And, as we have noted, being able to "see" the sale is often listed as one of the reasons producers shift from terminal market selling to selling through auctions. As the auction markets are usually closer to the producer than the terminal markets are, transportation, shrink, and other marketing costs are usually less at the auctions than at the terminals. The decentralization of the meat packing industry has resulted in an increase of local packer buyers who often find the auction a good place to buy livestock. The number of auction markets and the volume of business per auction have therefore been increasing.

In spite of their growth, in 1955 the typical livestock auction market was a relatively small-scale operation (Table 17). Over 50% were small auction markets, that is, markets selling fewer than 10,000 marketing units annually.[6] Only about a

Table 17. Species of Livestock Sold by Size of Auction Market, 1955

Size of Auction Market *	Number of Auction Markets		All Livestock (Marketing Units)	Cattle	Calves	Hogs	Sheep and Lambs
Small:							
Under 10,000	1,330	57.3%	20.6%	17.7%	26.8%	29.8%	15.5%
Medium:							
10,000–24,999	720	31.0	38.0	35.8	42.4	44.9	36.0
Large:							
25,000–39,999	163	7.0	17.0	17.7	15.4	13.2	27.0
40,000–54,999	53	2.3	8.3	9.5	5.8	5.2	5.7
55,000 and above	56	2.4	16.1	19.3	9.6	6.9	15.8
All large	272	11.7%	41.4%	48.5%	30.8%	25.3%	48.5%
Total	2,322	100.0%	100.0%	100.0%	100.0%	100.0%	100.0%

* Size classification based on the annual marketing units handled for each auction.

Source: U. S. Agricultural Marketing Service, Marketing Research Report No. 223, "Livestock Auction Markets in the United States," by Gerald Engelman and Betty Sue Pence. (Washington, Government Printing Office, March 1958), p. 16.

fifth of all livestock was sold through these small auctions. Medium-sized markets, selling between 10,000 and 25,000 units, sold slightly under two-fifths of all auction livestock. Markets of this size make up 31% of the total. The few large markets selling over 25,000 units sold slightly over two-fifths

[6] One marketing unit or equivalent equals 1 head of cattle, 3 calves, 4 hogs, or 10 sheep and lambs.

of all auction livestock. Only 12% of the auction markets are this large.[7]

Operating costs per marketing unit handled in the larger auctions were generally lower than similar costs in smaller auctions.[8] This was due to the relatively high percentage of the total cost made up by fixed costs—land, building, and equipment. A small auction well-located, engineered, and managed may have lower costs per unit than a larger unit that is poorly laid out, located, and operated, but this is the exception rather than the rule.[9] The larger auction market usually attracts both more and larger buyers, which makes the larger auction a better market for livestock than a smaller auction with fewer, smaller buyers.

The number of livestock auction markets is likely to decline after the rapid expansion of the late 1950's. An adjustment might be expected for at least three interrelated reasons. First, many auctions were started in locations whose potential sales volumes were too small to support a livestock market over a long period of time. Second, the struggle for volume means that as some auctions are successful they will attract volume away from others. In recent years, some auctions have been able to grow at the expense of the large terminal markets. As the terminal market volume tends to stabilize, however, the growth potential for auctions is more likely to be through expanded territorial coverage and a shifting of business from other auctions. Finally, producers who raise livestock in quan-

[7] U. S. Agricultural Marketing Service, Marketing Research Report No. 223, "Livestock Auction Markets in the United States," (Washington, Government Printing Office, March 1958), p. 16.

[8] Texas Agricultural Experiment Station, Misc. Publication No. 118, "Texas Livestock Auction Markets" (College Station, Texas, December 1954), p. 4; also U. S. Department of Agriculture, Farmer Cooperative Service, Gen. Report 39, "Improving Livestock Marketing Efficiency," by Ira Stevens and R. L. Fox (Washington, Government Printing Office, January 1958), p. iv.

[9] Texas Agricultural Experiment Station, Misc. Publication No. 93, "Texas Livestock Auction Markets—Methods and Facilities" (College Station, Texas, April 1953), p. 3; also Stevens and Fox, "Improving Livestock Marketing Efficiency," p. iv.

tity will probably prefer to sell their livestock direct or through marketing organizations, thus bypassing the auction markets. As production units become larger, the local auction will be confronted with dwindling supplies of livestock. If this analysis is correct, the livestock auction industry will experience a period of intense competition with relatively few firms emerging as larger, more dominant organizations in any one area. The number of auction markets will decline, but the average volume of each will increase.

Initially the impact of these changes will be felt in the Corn Belt. Later, auctions in other regions will go through the same adjustments. The successful auctions will cover enough territory and have sufficient volume to attract a variety of buyers including, in many areas, order buyers for shipment to distant markets. The auction markets probably will be operated more than one day per week; three days or more per week may become common practice. In addition, the auction personnel will advise feeders on when and what to produce and sell and will supply producers with information on feeding, care, and management problems.

Direct Selling by Producers

The uptrend in direct selling began after World War I. Direct selling is now the dominant means of marketing hogs in many areas of the North Central States, the principal hog producing region of the country. Direct selling also is an important outlet for slaughter cattle in many areas, particularly in the Pacific Coast States.

Improvements in trucks for livestock and in highways meant that farmers were no longer tied to outlets located at important railroad terminals or river crossings. Livestock could move in any direction. Improved communications, such as the radio and telephone, and an expanded market information service also spurred the development of direct selling of livestock, especially in sales to packers.[10]

[10] Phillips and Engleman, "Market Outlets," p. 10.

Direct selling, like selling at auctions, appeals to producers in that it permits them to observe and exercise some control over selling. Consignment to distant terminal markets at times represents an irreversible commitment to sell. Larger and more specialized livestock farmers feel competent to sell their livestock direct.

Organizations that buy livestock direct from producers and then resell it are classified into two general types: packers and nonpackers. The nonpackers include dealers, trucker buyers, feed suppliers, and producer group and cooperative marketing organizations.

Packers

In order to assure a supply of particular qualities of livestock, some packers buy direct from producers at the packing plants and at the packers' country buying points. These country buying points are fixed places of business, where there are pens and scales, to which livestock are delivered directly by farmers. Cattle, hogs, and sheep are often bought by packer-buyers who travel the country from farm to farm and from feedlot to feedlot making their bids on the livestock they inspect. In the North Central States 32% of the hogs marketed were sold direct to packers in 1956.

Packer buyers purchase approximately 15% of all livestock marketed by producers and the figure is expected to rise. Over the 1940–1956 period in the North Central States there appeared to be little change in the relative number of cattle purchased directly by packers but the proportion of hogs increased 10%.[11]

Other Livestock Marketing Organizations

Even though some producers may find it desirable to sell their livestock directly to packers or processors, others will find it more advantageous to concentrate on production and leave the marketing to some other specialized firm. These special-

[11] *Livestock Marketing in the North Central Region*, pp. 25, 44.

ized firms may be: (1) strictly marketing firms, such as dealers and trucker buyers, that take title to the livestock, (2) feed suppliers or others who have supplied the producer with inputs under contract, (3) producer marketing organizations that purchase the livestock from producers and then sell to packers, processors, or others (included here would be cooperative livestock marketing organizations or other groups of individuals that buy livestock outright from producers for resale), or (4) some combination of these three.

Marketing Firms. There are several services that a specialized marketing firm might perform for the producer better than he could for himself. The larger volume of livestock accumulated by a specialized marketing firm enables it to tap markets not easily accessible to individual producers. Because of its size a marketing firm also can afford to hire personnel specialized in the marketing of particular kinds and species of livestock. The large volume of product controlled by the organization permits more flexibility in grading and sorting, thus performing a better job than individual producers in meeting and satisfying buyer demands. A strong specialized marketing firm would have greater bargaining power than individual producers in relation to meat packers and other functional groups in the meat economy. Specialized marketing firms can also assist producers by performing such services as making breeding or feeding stock available, supplying management help in both production and marketing, and securing credit to meet capital needs.

Truckers and Dealers. The importance of the trucker buyer diminished as his function was assumed by other agencies. Improved market news and better transportation to livestock markets has led to this decline. The local dealer markets have in a sense replaced the trucker buyer who bought livestock at the farm. The local dealers with country buying operations include contract buyers, who buy for later delivery, order buyers, purchasing on order for others, and a variety of speculative buyers. Some of these country buyers purchase livestock at fixed establishments similar to packer-owned country buying points.

The essentially local nature of most livestock dealer markets may be a limiting factor on sales volume. As dealers expand their operations over a broader geographical area to attain increased volume, however, some of the advantages of a local operation are lost.

Dealer markets as an outlet for cattle and hogs declined in importance in the North Central States from 1940 to 1956.[12] These markets will probably continue to account for only a small percentage of the total marketing receipts as direct sales to packers, and sales through producer livestock marketing organizations increase.

Feed Companies. Feed companies or others in control of supplies may market livestock produced under integrated arrangements with livestock feeders. Although many of the integration plans or contracts used in the past have not included assistance in marketing the livestock, it seems likely that in the future more of the contracts between feed companies and others and producers will call for marketing assistance.

The feed companies and feed suppliers undoubtedly will assume a more important role in the production and marketing of livestock in the future than they had in the past. The use of commercial feeds and feed additives will continue to expand. The proportion of livestock feed in the form of concentrates has increased for all species,[13] but is particularly high for hogs. And an increasing proportion of the concentrates has been in the form of "formula feeds," [14] the principal type of feed sold by feed companies. These changes in livestock feed-

---

12 *Ibid.*
13 See Appendix Table 19 for feed consumption.
14 See Appendix Table 20 for outputs of manufactured feed.

ing are likely to continue. The feed companies will therefore become more interested in closer ties with hog, cattle, and sheep and lamb producers as outlets for their feed.

There will be an expansion of production on contract between the feed supplier and the producer. In newer production areas (i.e., outside the Corn Belt), where the marketing system is not well-developed, the contracts will probably call for assistance in marketing as well as management. The feed company may establish livestock marketing agencies of its own or utilize existing agencies. As the volume of livestock produced under contract increases, it seems likely that new subsidiary marketing organizations will be formed by feed companies or others integrating their operations with the production of livestock.

Cooperative Marketing Organizations. Producer cooperative livestock marketing organizations, which buy livestock from producers and then resell to meat packers, processors, and others, have been in operation for many years.[15] Through educational programs, and other means, the managements of these associations have had limited control over marketing (for example, time of marketing, quality, and kind of animals marketed). Some of these organizations have shifted to a system of contract production with their members in order to increase the control by the organization over products marketed. The provisions of the contracts vary widely. In the future such contracts are likely to give the marketing organizations more and more control over the amount, kind, and quality of the product and the time of marketing. A marketing organization of this type may find it desirable to limit membership to those who produce a certain quantity or quality of livestock. It should be emphasized that such an organization has a much better chance of succeeding if the management is

[15] See Appendix Table 21 for value of livestock and livestock products marketed by cooperative organizations.

of the highest caliber and if the volume is sufficient to allow the organization to operate effectively in the market. The two conditions are not entirely unrelated in that it is usually the larger organization which can attract the more capable management.

The marketing of livestock through cooperative organizations will increase between 1959 and 1975. The rate of growth will depend upon how quickly the prospective leadership and membership of such cooperatives see the need for and the potential advantages of large-scale livestock buying and selling organizations. The members must also have a clear understanding of the functions, possibilities, and limitations of the organization. They must plan ahead a good deal in order that the organization be able to cope satisfactorily with management, membership relations, capital, and other problems likely to arise in the future. Above all, they must be willing to delegate to the cooperative those powers needed if the organization is to be successful. Livestock producers will not automatically patronize or join cooperative marketing groups. Cooperative organizations must do as good a job, or better, of marketing the product, providing needed services not provided by other market outlets for livestock, or both, if such cooperatives are to grow and prosper.

The size and complexity of the cooperative buying and marketing organizations of the future will probably be beyond the managerial capacity of present cooperative managers. Perhaps the capacity of present managers can be extended through training programs or outside assistance. If not, new management personnel must be trained.

Further Integration by Marketing Agencies

Present indications are that the capital needs of agriculture are going to increase greatly between 1959 and 1975. Livestock producers will certainly feel the need for added capital, particularly if they expand their units to more nearly optimum economic size. A marketing organization with control over the sale of product would be in a good position either to grant or to arrange for credit for its producer patrons. If the organization is willing to guarantee the loans, it should be able to get credit on more favorable terms than individual producers.

In order to perform its various services effectively, the marketing agency may find it desirable to contract both for the sale and for the procurement of the livestock. Through the use of contracts the management of marketing agencies could do a more effective job of aligning supply and demand particularly with respect to kind and quality of animals marketed and time of marketing. Pricing arrangements might be based strictly upon bargaining between the parties involved, or some formula might be worked out that specified prices in relation to terminal market or other market quotations such as the wholesale meat price at Chicago. In many places, livestock prices are sometimes calculated on the basis of wholesale meat prices with agreed-upon conversion factors. This method of pricing livestock produced and sold under contract may become more widespread.

The specialized livestock marketing agencies of the future may be revamped models of old organizations or they may be entirely new organizations. In general, such marketing organizations will market a much larger volume of livestock than their predecessors and will have more control over quality, kind, and time of sale of the product.

Feeding by Marketing Agencies

There will be mounting pressure for marketing agencies to engage in livestock feeding themselves. In part, this pressure will arise because of the relative inefficiency of current livestock production. Most comparisons of attainable returns from livestock feeding with data from so-called average feeders show considerable differences in costs and returns at a given level of prices. Feed companies, packers, and others find it inviting to calculate possible returns from well-managed, efficient feeding operations. Such calculations usually assume that livestock prices will be at a level that will keep the so-called average producer in business. Initially this assumption may prove correct, but as more of the livestock is produced in larger scale units, the advantage of the larger units over the average units is likely to decline.

A livestock marketing organization, particularly a cooperative organization, going into livestock production may experience difficulty because the organization would be in competition with its own members or patrons. A large company operating over a wide geographical area would be able to operate differently in the various regions which it services. In one region the livestock might be produced by the organization while in another region the organization might contract or buy the livestock from established producers. In the cash grain areas, feed companies or marketing organizations might go into the feeding business with relatively few producer relations problems since livestock have not been produced in large quantities in these areas. In fact, feeding operations there might be regarded as another market for the grain produced in the area. It would be more difficult for a marketing organization to go into the feeding business in an area that already has high livestock production.

Meat Packing and Processing. Many farmers and farm groups have been interested in marketing livestock through cooperative meat packing plants. Discussions of integration possibilities in the livestock industry often include the idea of farmer-owned and controlled processing facilities on either a direct ownership or a contract basis. At least one state livestock marketing organization has an arrangement whereby livestock is in effect slaughtered by a packer for the account of a cooperative chain of grocery stores. Another producer group has an arrangement with a packer to process meat on a custom basis for the account of a local grocery chain. Other farmer cooperatives have been actively interested in the possibilities of getting into the meat packing business.

In 1959 there were three medium-sized farmer cooperative meat processing plants in operation. Between 1930 and 1955 thirteen plants were organized,[16] but by 1959 only two were still in operation.[17] Another plant began operations in 1959. Cooperative processing plants have failed for many reasons: (1) lack of sufficient operating capital, (2) lack of farmer support, (3) inexperienced and consequently inefficient management, (4) lack of confidence in management by patrons, (5) unsatisfactory sales outlets, (6) inadequate and irregular supplies of livestock, (7) old, worn-out plants, and (8) unfavorable freight rates for dressed meats.[18]

The fact that most of the earlier cooperative meat packing plants failed does not mean that every such venture is doomed. But it does mean that groups of livestock producers, or even established cooperatives, should investigate potential difficulties thoroughly before making any final plans to set up a meat packing business.[19]

Feed companies and other groups controlling supplies of livestock would face some of the same difficulties as cooperatives in moving into the meat packing and processing business. It seems probable that feed suppliers will be content to sell the livestock they control to specialized meat packers and processors through independent marketing organizations or their own marketing subsidiaries. It may be possible for the marketing organization to sell meat directly to retail outlets by having the livestock custom slaughtered. There would be

[16] U. S. Department of Agriculture, Farmer Cooperative Service, General Report No. 29, "Farmer Meat Packing Enterprises in the United States," by R. L. Fox (Washington, Government Printing Office, April 1957), p. ii.

[17] Correspondence with C. G. Randell, Chief, Livestock and Wool Branch, Farmer Cooperative Service, U. S. Department of Agriculture.

[18] R. L. Fox, "Farmer Meat Packing," pp. 3–4.

[19] *Ibid.*, p. ii.

many disadvantages to such a plan, however. Meat packers and processors working wholly on commission might not provide a consistently high quality product. Furthermore, there might be delays or errors in deliveries to retail outlets. On the other hand, custom slaughtering may enable a marketing organization to capitalize on superior quality production or products that will command a premium in the market. Through the custom arrangement, the marketing organization obtains the use of processing facilities without providing the huge sums of capital that would be needed to build or buy such facilities. It seems probable that any marketing organization that finds it advantageous to market meat directly to retail outlets will also find it advantageous to have its own slaughtering and processing facilities.

Chapter VII

ADJUSTMENTS IN LIVESTOCK PRODUCTION

LIVESTOCK ARE produced in virtually every part of the United States. On January 1, 1959, there were 97 million cattle and calves, 57 million hogs, and 33 million sheep and lambs on farms in the United States.[1] The number of cattle and calves was at an all-time high on January 1, 1959. The peak year for hogs was 1944 (84 million) and the peak year for sheep and lambs was 1942 (56 million).[2] During the period 1955 to 1958 the proportion of total liveweight production of livestock made up by the various species was 57% cattle, 40% hogs, and 3% sheep and lambs.

Total livestock production is the result of management decisions made by millions of livestock producers at various lengths of time before the animals are marketed and slaughtered. Available and prospective feed supplies, available labor, relative prices, and other factors influence such management decisions. Interregional competition and the principle of comparative advantage determine in part where the feed and livestock will be produced.

Production Potential and Estimates of Future Production

In projections prepared by the United States Department of Agriculture [3] it is estimated that beef output per cow will

[1] See Appendix Table 22 for number of livestock on farms 1955 to 1959 by species.
[2] U. S. Agricultural Marketing Service, Statistical Bulletin No. 230, *Livestock and Meat Statistics, 1957* (Washington, Government Printing Office, July 1958), pp. 3, 4.
[3] U. S. Agricultural Research Service, Neg. 58(10)–2594, 2595.

increase about 7% between 1957 and 1975. This compares with a 6% increase between 1939–1941 and 1957. Pork production is expected to increase slightly more than beef, with a 27% increase in pork per litter expected between 1957 and 1975. During the period 1939–1941 to 1957 a 16% increase in pork per litter was recorded.

The number of pounds of feed or the number of feed units required to produce a pound of hog is expected to decrease about 15% from 1957 to 1975 compared with essentially no change during the period 1939–1941 to 1957. The pounds of feed required per pound of gain in cattle are expected to drop from 9.6 pounds in 1957 to 8.8 pounds by 1975. This 8% improvement compares with a 3% change during the period 1939–1941 to 1957.

Increased use of fertilizer, improved varieties, and other improved practices will continue to step up crop yield per acre between 1957 and 1975. The U. S. Department of Agriculture estimates that if farmers continue to adopt new practices at the current rate, by 1975 the yield will be about 40% above 1951–1953 and more than 25% above 1957. These results indicate that further additions to crop yields may be the primary means of meeting farm output needs by 1975.[4] Since no allowance has been made for new developments in technology, these figures for potential changes in crop yields are minimal. Actual crop yields are very likely to exceed these estimates.

The probable balancing of the expected increases in total consumption of agricultural products including meats with potential production increases indicates that agriculture can meet the projected output needs for 1975 with relative ease if the projected crop and livestock yields and levels of feeding efficiency are reached. If a more effective means could be found for achieving optimum use of land, the present land

[4] G. T. Barton and R. F. Daly, "Prospects for Agriculture in a Growing Economy," address at a Conference on Problems and Policies of American Agriculture at Iowa State College, Ames, Iowa, October 27–31, 1958, p. 13 (mimeographed).

96   The Meat Economy

base would be more than adequate. With consolidation of small units, the total land needed would be essentially the same as the 526 million acres used in 1951–1953.[5] Under present conditions, however, acres of cropland and cropland pas-

Figure 5

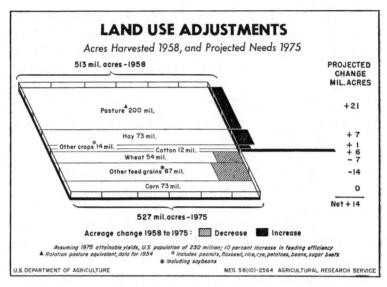

ture in addition to that in use in 1956 would be required (Figure 5). On the other hand, it has been estimated that there will be a net of 30 million acres of new cropland added to the cropland base between the early 1950's and 1975, if public programs and related farm improvements continue at about the same rate as in the 1945–1955 decade.[6] It seems likely that

[5] H. L. Stewart, "Prospects for Adjustment in Production and Resource Use," address at the 36th Annual Outlook Conference of the U. S. Agricultural Marketing Service, Farm Economics Research Division, Washington, November 18, 1958.

[6] U. S. Agricultural Research Service, Agriculture Information Bulletin No. 140, "Agricultural Land Resources in the United States, with Special Reference to Present and Potential Cropland and Pastures," by Hugh H. Wooten and James R. Anderson (Washington, Government Printing Office, June 1955).

foreseeable demand can easily be met during the period between now and 1975.

The labor force in agriculture also will be more than adequate to meet our production needs by 1975. If the trends during the 1947–1957 decade in output per man-hour continue, 1975 production needs can be met with one-third fewer man-hours of farm labor than were used in 1957.

The predictions of supply possibilities were made mainly on the basis of present technology with no allowance for new developments. The predictions were tempered by an allowance for management limitations and other factors that have tended to retard adoption of improved practices in the past. There is no apparent reason, however, why the development of new technology should not proceed in the future as fast as or faster than in the past. There are a number of good reasons for believing that the rate of adoption of improved techniques is likely to be more rapid in the future; for example, the increasing number of commercial farms as compared with smaller, lower income operations, the improved level of managerial capacity of farm operators, increases and improvements in management help from nonfarm sources, and a host of other changes affecting agricultural production will tend to speed up the rate of adoption of technological developments in agriculture. If new developments are discovered and adopted, and if it is assumed that new developments will be adopted somewhat faster in the future than they have been in the past, the supplies of livestock products in 1975 will be more than ample to meet the projected demand at the assumed price levels. Unless demand can be expanded beyond the projected levels, therefore, livestock prices will probably be relatively lower in 1975 than in 1956.

This is not to say that the income of livestock producers would necessarily be less in 1975. New technology, larger units, and other developments are forces pushing toward lower per unit cost. There can be little question, however, that the relatively lower prices would make it more difficult for those producers who cannot or do not adjust their operations to the changed conditions to continue production in the long run.

Another effect of a market situation in which supply tends to increase at a faster rate than demand is an almost perpetual buyers' market. Consumers have a wide variety of all kinds of meat available to them at prices seemingly in line with or lower than prices for other commodities. In such a situation it takes considerable effort on the part of the retailers to increase the movement of meat even slightly. The retailer is contacted by many suppliers who are eager to help fill his needs. Under the supply-demand relation likely to prevail in the 1960's and early 1970's, retail buyers will be able to be very discriminating in the meat they buy.

Location of Livestock Production and Slaughter

Livestock production has been concentrated in two areas of the United States—the Corn Belt and the West. Of the total number of commercial livestock farms [7] in the United States in 1954, 47% were located in the Corn Belt and 35% in the West.[8] Since the 1947–1949 period, however, the production of livestock has increased more rapidly in the South than in any other region (Table 18). Thus while the Corn Belt and the West have been the most important areas of livestock production in the past, other regions also produce large numbers of some species.

[7] Commercial farms are farms which have an annual value of products sold of $1,200 or more, or farms where the value of products sold is between $250 and $1,199 and the farmer works off the farm less than 100 days and the total value of farm products sold was greater than the income received by him and members of his family from nonfarm sources. Commercial livestock farms are commercial farms with 50% or more of the value of products sold being livestock.

[8] U. S. Bureau of the Census, *1954 Census of Agriculture* (Washington, Government Printing Office, 1956), Vol. III, Part 9, Chapter VI, p. 8 and Chapter VII, p. 7.

Table 18.   Index of Total Meat Animal * Production by Regions,
Selected Years, 1930–1957
(1947–1949 = 100)

Year	New Eng- land	Middle At- lantic	E.N. Cent.	W.N. Cent.	South At- lantic	E.S. Cent.	W.S. Cent.	Moun- tain	Pa- cific
1957	97	102	122	119	134	131	112	122	131
1956	102	106	121	121	132	128	123	125	138
1955	113	119	124	129	131	123	121	125	141
1954	116	116	117	122	125	116	117	124	131
1953	123	121	114	116	123	110	115	121	127
1952	118	122	117	117	123	111	117	119	122
1951	110	115	116	120	114	110	114	116	118
1950	104	109	111	111	106	106	110	104	108
1945	108	101	102	104	101	95	108	107	104
1940	102	95	98	86	81	79	85	89	96
1935	93	80	66	62	70	68	59	74	79
1930	99	83	70	90	64	54	64	81	71

* Cattle and Calves, Sheep and Lambs, and Hogs.

Source: U. S. Agricultural Marketing Service, Statistical Bulletin No.
233, "Changes in Farm Production Efficiency, Supplement
#1" (Washington, Government Printing Office, August
1958), pp. 6–23.

Cattle and Calves

In 1958 the North Central region accounted for approximately 45% of all cattle and calves on farms.[9] Another 29%
of the cattle and calves were in the Western region, including
Texas and Oklahoma. "About two-thirds of the cattle and
calves that are shipped from western growing areas are sold
for immediate slaughter, the remaining one-third are shipped
into the Corn Belt and other states to be fed to heavier weight
before slaughter." [10]

Cattle feeding is concentrated in the Corn Belt states with
between 40% and 50% of all cattle and calves on feed in the

[9] Calculated from Livestock and Meat Statistics, 1957, p. 9; see Appendix
Table 22.
[10] Geoffrey S. Shepherd, Marketing Farm Products (Ames, Iowa, Iowa
State College Press, 3rd ed., 1955), p. 324.

States of Ohio, Indiana, Illinois, Iowa, and Missouri. In 1958
the North Central States accounted for approximately 75%
of all cattle and calves on feed. These feeding operations included animals produced locally as well as animals produced
in other regions. Perhaps the greatest change in the location of

Table 19.   Cattle and Calves on Feed, Selected Regions,
January 1, 1950, to 1958

| | | North Central States | | | | Western States | |
| | | | West North Central | | | | |
Year	Penna.	East North Cent.	Corn Belt *	Plains †	Texas & Okla.	Calif.	Other
1959 ‡	1%	20%	32%	20%	3%	8%	16%
1958	1	23	33	18	3	7	15
1957	2	23	31	17	4	8	15
1956	1	23	31	18	4	8	15
1955	1	22	31	20	3	8	15
1954	2	23	31	21	4	6	13
1953	2	20	32	23	4	6	13
1952	2	20	30	21	5	8	14
1951	2	21	33	21	5	5	13
1950	2	22	34	21	5	4	12

* Minnesota, Iowa, Missouri.
† North Dakota, South Dakota, Nebraska, and Kansas.
‡ Estimated.
Source: Calculated from Appendix Table 23.

cattle feeding has been the increase in the Far West, especially California (Table 19). Since 1954 over 20% of the cattle and calves on feed have been in the West. This compares
with 9%–12% of the national total in the 1930–1935 period.
The shift in the location of cattle feeding resulted from the
considerable expansion in both the size and the number of
feedlots in the Mountain States and in California. Many of
the Western feedlots were built to supply slaughter animals
for western packers.

Approximately 45% of the total beef production is accounted for by fed cattle.[11] The proportion of fed cattle is likely to increase and there will be changes in the location of the feeding. Cattle feeding will continue to increase in the West, although at a somewhat slower rate than in the 1948–1958 decade. Cattle feeding in the South also will increase, at least for locally consumed beef. The declines in the acreage of typical Southern crops, such as tobacco and cotton, and the increases in the production of pasture, hay, and grain sorghums make it likely that greater numbers of cattle will be fed in the South.

While part of the expansion in cattle feeding will be in packer owned or contracted lots, the development of privately owned lots will continue. In spite of the forces pushing for increases in livestock feeding and production in other areas of the country, the bulk of the cattle will continue to be produced and fed in the Corn Belt.

The slaughtering of cattle is also concentrated in the North Central States. In 1957 approximately 53% of all cattle were slaughtered there.[12] The West accounted for an additional 18% of cattle slaughter. Much of the increase in the proportion of total cattle slaughter carried on in the West is attributable to the increases in cattle feeding in this area.

A comparison of the net marketings and slaughter of beef by states indicates that the states with a surplus of marketings over slaughter are South Dakota, Oklahoma, Montana, and Texas. The states where slaughter exceeds marketings are California, Illinois, Wisconsin, Michigan, Ohio, Pennsylvania, and New York. In some of these areas where slaughter exceeds marketings of beef animals, the difference is made up by lo-

---

[11] Fed cattle are those that have received some grain or other concentrate feeds. They are distinguished from grass cattle, produced almost exclusively on grass and roughage. Some cattle are fed for between 30 and 60 days, some for a year or so. See Appendix Table 24 for percentage of the beef production that is fed, 1945–1955.

[12] See Appendix Table 25 for percentage of total cattle slaughter by region, 1947–1957.

cally marketed dairy cows. In general, however, the cattle move from the West to the North Central States to be slaughtered and processed.

In the future, if the ratio of freight rates on live animals to rates on meat remains the same, cattle slaughter will continue to be located chiefly in the areas where cattle production and feeding are concentrated. Cattle slaughter will therefore continue to be heavily concentrated in the Corn Belt states, but it will be located in areas of the Corn Belt where the livestock are rather than in the metropolitan centers. As feeding increases in the South and West, the proportion of cattle slaughtered in these areas will increase. The proportion of cattle slaughtered in the Northeast will decline because of the expected decline in the number of dairy animals in this area and because of the anticipated relative decline in proportion of total population.

Hogs

Hog production has tended to be concentrated in that portion of the United States best suited to the production of feed grain—the Corn Belt. Since 1930 hog production has become more concentrated in the central Corn Belt states of Ohio, Indiana, Iowa, and Missouri. In 1957 these states produced approximately 55% of the pigs saved in the United States as compared with 44% to 46% prior to World War II.[13] Most of these relative increases in hog production in the central Corn Belt states came from the plains states of North Dakota, South Dakota, Nebraska, and Kansas. The percentage of total pigs saved in the plains states declined from about 20% in 1930 to less than 10% in the postwar years.

In the late 1950's there were slight increases in the proportion of hog production and pigs saved in the South, particularly the South Atlantic and East South Central States.[14] As

[13] See Appendix Table 26 for the percentage of total pigs saved by regions.
[14] See Appendix Table 27 for hog production and number of hogs on farms by region, 1954 and 1957.

with cattle production, these increases in the South have been chiefly the result of increased grain production in this area. Although there have been some minor fluctuations in the intervening years between 1930 and 1957, other areas of the country have retained about the same relative position in hog production.

Future hog production will continue to be located primarily in the Corn Belt states. Minor increases in the relative share of hog production will continue in the South. For the most part, new hog production outside the Corn Belt will come from facilities owned by or under the control of feed companies, packing plants, or marketing organizations. Few individuals in these areas will have the capital or "know-how" to go into hog production without outside assistance.

In the Corn Belt hog production has been and will continue to be a major enterprise on many farms. The "know-how" to produce hogs, coupled with the availability of relatively cheap feed, gives the Corn Belt an advantage over other areas of the country in hog production. Contracts covering the production and marketing of hogs will become more common in the Corn Belt as well as in other newer production areas.

The location of hog slaughter has closely followed the location of hog production. Sixty-six per cent of total U. S. hog slaughter in 1957 was in the North Central States.[15] Since 1947 there has been a small relative decline in hog slaughter in the North Central States and small increases in the South. Hog slaughter has been increasing in the South Atlantic and East South Central States. The largest difference between location of hog slaughter and of production has been in the Northeast. In this region approximately 2% of the total number of hogs were produced, but close to 10% of the hogs were slaughtered. These were primarily hogs produced in the North Central States. In the West there has also been a larger proportion of slaughter than production. Therefore, even though a large proportion of hog slaughter has been concentrated in

[15] See Appendix Table 28 for hog slaughter by region 1947–1957.

the North Central States, there has been a sizable movement of live hogs from the Corn Belt to other regions.

The location of hog slaughter will continue to follow the pattern of hog production closely. There will be increases in hog slaughtering in the South and in the Corn Belt areas where hog production will increase. Many of the new slaughtering facilities in the Corn Belt will replace obsolete facilities presently in operation and therefore will not represent a regional shift in the location of slaughtering.

Sheep and Lambs

As sheep and lambs are primarily roughage consuming animals, their production has been chiefly in the Western range areas. In 1958 the Western States accounted for approximately 44% of all sheep and lamb production.[16] In recent years there appears to have been a shift in the location of sheep and lamb production towards the East. This shift has come about because of alternative employment available to the sheep ranchers and sheepherders of the Western area, higher lambing rates outside of the West, and several other factors.

In the North Central States, Iowa and South Dakota particularly, more lambs were saved in 1958 than in the 1946–1955 period. During this same period the numbers of lambs saved in the Mountain and West South Central States declined. This trend toward farm flock production rather than range production is likely to continue, especially if there is an increase in amount of roughage produced outside the West.

With the exception of California, the production, slaughter, and consumption of sheep and lambs are each concentrated in different parts of the United States. In 1957, 28% of the slaughter and 44% of the production was in the West, and 9% of the slaughter and about 21% of production was in the South. The sheep and lambs produced in the South and

---

[16] See Appendix Table 29 for the percentage of total lambs saved by regions.

West in large part were shipped either to the North Central or to the Northeastern States for slaughter.

During the ten-year period, 1947–1957, the percentage of total sheep and lamb slaughter increased from 19% to 28% in the West, and decreased from 40% to 32% in the West North Central States.[17] These shifts in the location of sheep and lamb slaughter are likely to continue, though at a slower rate. The relative increases in sheep and lamb production in the West North Central region will slow down and eventually stabilize the rate of decrease in slaughtering in this area. The decline in production in the West will tend to slow down the rate of increase in slaughter there. For the most part, however, sheep and lambs will continue to be produced in the West, slaughtered in the Midwest, and consumed on the East and West coasts.

The Size and Efficiency of Production Units

Research has indicated that there is considerable variation in the efficiency of livestock production as it is carried on by different producers. These differences arise in part from differences in the sizes of production units.

The numbers of livestock per farm and the numbers of livestock sold per farm, especially cattle and hogs, significantly increased from 1940 to 1954 (Tables 20 and 21). Even though the average size of livestock production units in the United States has increased, the average unit size is still small.

Despite this limitation there has been some improvement in the efficiency of livestock production. One commonly used measure of relative efficiency is production per man-hour. The production per man-hour of all major crops, milk cows, and poultry has increased at a much faster rate than the production of meat animals (Table 22). The increase in meat ani-

[17] Calculated from data presented in *Livestock and Meat Statistics, 1957*, p. 109.

Table 20. Number of Livestock on Farms per Farm, by Species, Selected Years, 1920–1954

Year	Cattle & Calves	Hogs & Pigs	Sheep & Lambs
1954	26.0	24.1	87.5
1950	18.9	18.5	97.9
1945	17.6	14.1	90.2
1935	12.4	9.4	76.1
1930	13.3	15.9	97.6
1920	12.4	12.2	65.0

Source: Calculated from data in the 1954 Census of Agriculture, Vol. II, Chapter VI, pp. 433–434.

Table 21. Number of Livestock Sold per Farm, by Species, Selected Years, 1939–1954

Year	Cattle & Calves	Hogs & Pigs	Sheep & Lambs
1954	17.0	40.3	77.3
1949	12.2	31.2	73.7
1944	12.0	32.4	86.4
1939	10.4	26.7	74.1

Source: Calculated from data in the 1954 Census of Agriculture, Vol. II, Chapter VI, p. 441.

mal production per man-hour has been slow for a number of reasons: (1) production per unit, such as pigs per sow or calves per cow, has not increased as fast as bushels per acre or milk per cow; [18] (2) the output per unit of feed for meat animals has not increased as fast as it has in poultry production; [19] (3) the feeding of meat animals has not been mechanized to the same extent as the production of other farm commodities.

[18] The percentage changes in output per animal from 1939–1941 to 1957 were as follows: beef per cow, 6%; pork per litter, 16%; milk per cow, 33%; eggs per layer 46%; from an address by H. L. Stewart, "Prospects for Adjustments in Production and Resource Use," before the Agricultural Outlook Conference, November 18, 1958, p. 16.

[19] See Appendix Table 30 for feed units consumed per head of livestock, 1930 to 1956.

Table 22. Index Numbers of Farm Production per Man-Hour
by Groups of Enterprises, Selected Years, 1930–1957
(1947–1949 = 100)

Year	Farm Output	Livestock and Livestock Products				All Crops
		Meat Animals	Milk Cows	Poultry	Total Livestock & Products	
1957	143	106	122	141	123	154
1956	136	107	121	140	124	141
1955	132	108	119	131	121	135
1954	127	106	116	129	118	129
1953	123	104	113	126	116	124
1952	120	104	110	118	114	123
1951	113	106	109	116	114	112
1950	112	104	107	110	109	115
1945	86	96	89	89	90	86
1940	70	94	77	79	81	69
1935	59	88	70	77	71	58
1930	54	92	75	73	76	52

Source: U. S. Agricultural Research Service, Statistical Bulletin No.
233, "Changes in Farm Production and Efficiency, A Summary Report" (Washington, Government Printing Office,
August 1958), pp. 25, 26.

Cattle and Calves

In 1954 approximately 3.6 million farms had cattle and
calves on hand,[20] but only 19% of these farms could be classified as commercial livestock farms.[21] These commercial livestock farms accounted for 45% of the total number of cattle
and calves. About four-fifths of these farms had less than 50
head of cattle. Thus even many of the commercial cattle production units have a relatively small number of cattle per farm.

As the figures for all cattle and calves on farms include
breeding stock as well as marketable animals, the numbers of
cattle and calves sold per farm more clearly point up the relatively small size of meat animal production units. Only about

[20] *1954 Census of Agriculture,* Vol. II, Chapter VI, p. 433.
[21] *Ibid.,* and Vol. III, part 9, Chapter VII, p. 6.

70% of all farms with cattle and calves, or 2.6 million farms, sold cattle and calves in 1954. All farms sold an average of 17 head per farm. Even the commercial livestock farms, which accounted for about half of the cattle and calves sold, averaged only 39 head sold per farm.[22] In Iowa, an area of high concentration of cattle production, about 87% of the farms reported sales of less than 40 head.[23]

The efficiency of cattle production has improved as measured by the production of beef per cow. The production of beef per cow was approximately 25% greater in 1958 than in 1948, two years at about comparable positions in the cattle cycle. Most of the increases in beef per cow can be ascribed to the shift from dairy cows to beef cows, which are more productive beef producers than dairy cows. In 1948 approximately 40% of all cows were beef cows, whereas in 1958 over 50% were beef cows.

Since cows can produce only one calf per year, opportunities for increasing output per cow in the future must center around changes in feeding and management. Breeding and management improvements may greatly influence the quality of the offspring. The production of beef per cow is expected to increase by 7% between 1958 and 1975. The efficiency of production as measured by the pounds of feed per pound of gain [24] will also improve. The pounds of feed per 100 pounds of beef is expected to decline by 8% by 1975.

Hogs

The size of hog production units has increased but still remains relatively small. In 1954 there were 2.4 million hog producers. About one-fourth of these producers had an average of only four hogs per farm. These small hog producers accounted for about 4% of all hogs. In contrast, about one-fifth of all

[22] See Appendix Table 31 for number of livestock on farms and sold by farms by type of farm.
[23] *1954 Census of Agriculture*, Vol. I, Part 9, p. 28.
[24] See Appendix Table 30.

hog producers—the commercial livestock producers—averaged 66 hogs per farm and accounted for 56% of all hogs on farms.

About one-third of all hog producers who sold hogs in 1954 sold less than 10 head, and approximately three-fourths of the producers sold less than 50 head. While the number of hogs sold per farm increased from 1944 to 1954, the increase was almost wholly confined to the North Central States.[25] In the South the number remained constant, and in the West it declined.

The typical hog production unit, even in the Corn Belt, has been small when compared with estimates of the volume needed to attain maximum efficiency.[26]

There also have been increases in the number of pigs saved per litter; it increased from between 5.5 and 6.0 in the 1920's and 1930's to over 7.0 in 1957. While the increase of only one pig per litter seems small, it was a significant change. In 1957 there were approximately the same number of sows as there were in 1930, but nearly 20% more pigs were produced. It is estimated that the number of pigs per litter will increase another 27% between 1958 and 1975.

There has been a modest decline in the weight of barrows and gilts marketed.[27] But this decrease has not been accompanied by improvements in feeding efficiency.[28] "Research has found that there is no difference in production costs between meat-type and fat-type hogs." [29] Thus, a shift to lighter weight

[25] *Livestock and Meat Situation*, September 1958, pp. 16 and 17.

[26] A number of estimates have been made on the make-up of a so-called efficient hog producing operation. Ronald Bauman of Purdue University suggests that "The efficiencies resulting from size are exhausted at the 50–60 sow, two litters per year level . . . He [the individual operator] can well go on beyond that point until his marginal returns become equal to his next best alternative." Fifty to 60 sows farrowing two litters per year of 7 pigs each would mean sales of 700–800 pigs per year per farm. On the other hand, some industry spokesmen list 1,000–1,500 hogs per man as an efficient operation.

[27] See Appendix Table 32 for average weight of barrows and gilts at Chicago, 1947–1957.

[28] See Appendix Table 30.

[29] South Dakota State College, Extension Circular No. 434, "Will the

hogs probably will not in itself greatly affect feeding efficiency. By 1975 hog feeding efficiency is expected to improve, with a 15% decrease in the pounds of feed per pound of liveweight production.

Sheep and Lambs

There has not been any significant increase in the number of sheep and lambs produced or sold per farm, but more sheep and lambs are produced per farm and sold per farm than either cattle or hogs. Of the 361,000 sheep and lamb producers in 1954, about four-fifths sold sheep and lambs that year. A higher percentage of the sheep and lamb production has been on commercial livestock farms than either cattle or hog production.

The shift in the location of sheep and lamb production away from the West will tend to decrease the average number on farms and animals sold per farm. Sheep production in the North Central States will continue to be chiefly a "side line" operation as compared with other livestock enterprises. Although the size of the average production unit will be smaller in the future, there will be increases in the efficiency of production. The large increases in the lamb production per ewe have been chiefly the result of increases in the lambs saved per ewe in the North Central States.[30]

Livestock Production in the Future

Many producers will be able to raise and market more livestock through greater specialization, adoption of improved technology for both crops and livestock, and the use of improved management practices. Increased economic pressure

---

Meat Type Hog Pay?" by E. Dailey and L. Bender (Brookings, S.D., South Dakota State College, May 1952), p. 2.

[30] See Appendix Table 29 for lambs saved per ewe by regions.

resulting from a "tightening" of the "cost-price squeeze" will be one factor tending to speed up the change to larger, more efficient production units. More intensified educational programs will shorten the lag between the discovery of new technology and its general adoption by producers. Since the level of managerial capacity of those producers who remain in livestock production will be higher, information about new developments will be heard by more receptive ears. All of these factors point toward a continuation and possible speeding up in the movement toward larger volume, more efficient production units.

Several developments may affect the kinds of animals that are produced. In the past demand for beef has centered around two qualities—the choice or good grade for fresh meat sales and lower grade beef for processed beef products.[31] The lower grade of beef has come mostly from cull dairy animals. The relative decline in the number of dairy animals, accompanied by an increasing demand for processed beef products, may open a new market for beef producers. A lower grade of beef could be produced with little grain and therefore might increase production in areas of the country where there is comparatively little grain. The use of improved meat tenderizers, which will become more widespread with increases in the freezing of meat, also may stimulate the production of lower grades of beef.

An increasing amount of meat freezing could also lead to the removal of waste and bone at the processing plant. Prices to producers, based on the pounds of edible meat rather than carcass weight or live weight, may be introduced under such a system. A development of this nature would greatly affect the kind and type of beef produced.

Many devices for identifying easily and quickly the fat thickness of pork and beef have been introduced. If a cheap, quick,

[31] See Appendix Table 33 for head of cattle by grades each month, 1957.

reliable method to determine quality is found, the drive for improved meat quality will be speeded up. The selection of breeding stock also would be simplified.

The extent of development of "integrated" production as opposed to strictly farm production depends for the most part on how rapidly new technology and management techniques are adopted by the producers. If producers in general are relatively slow to adopt cost saving techniques, contract feeding will expand rapidly. On the other hand, if the average producer adopts new techniques rapidly, improves management, and otherwise improves efficiency, there will be relatively less feeding by nonfarm firms. Even though there will be a step-up in the rate of adoption of new technology as far as individual producers are concerned, livestock production by integrated firms on large-scale production units will increase both in total and in comparison with production by individual producers.

Production costs of the larger production units of the future will in general be lower than similar costs of units today.[32] As a greater share of the production comes from larger, lower cost units, livestock prices will tend to move downward. Profit margins of the relatively high cost producers will be reduced and producers will then face the alternatives of adjusting their operation so as to lower costs, shifting to more remunerative enterprises, moving to employment outside agriculture, or continuing livestock production at a relatively lower income. In terms of the numbers of producers involved, the adjustment problem is staggering. For example, 75,000 farms selling 1,000 hogs each could have supplied the total number of hogs marketed in the United States in 1957. Even if each farm produced and sold only 500 hogs, 150,000 farms would have been required. These estimates of the needed number of farms are substantially smaller than the 2.4 million producers raising

[32] Production costs are used here to refer to physical inputs such as hours of labor, pounds of feed, etc., per pound of product. Dollar production costs will, of course, depend upon the physical inputs and price level changes.

hogs in 1954. Similar comparisons show that if cattle producers sold on the average 300 head per farm in 1957, 108,000
producers could have supplied the 32.5 million head of cattle
sold in the United States. This compares with 3.6 million cattle producers in 1954. The average production per farm will
not be as large as 500 or 1,000 hogs or 300 cattle by 1975, but
there will be considerably more producers feeding and marketing these numbers of animals than during the 1950's. The
average output per farm firm engaged in livestock production
could easily double or triple by 1975.

There will be an increasing concentration in production,
with the larger farms producing an increasing share of total
production. If past trends continue, most farm firms that will
cease operating will be farms of smaller size. The striving to
improve efficiency and size of production unit will create
many problems for livestock producers—these problems center around the capital needs, managerial capacity, and marketing ability.

New Capital Needs

Nearly all firms producing livestock will lack both working
and investment capital as they expand in volume. Only a small
percentage of the farm firms will be able to accumulate the
needed capital from within the operations of the farm business. Operators of many livestock production units, therefore,
are going to be looking for outside sources of capital. Capital
may be forthcoming from a variety of sources, such as banks,
cooperative lending agencies, government lending agencies,
marketing organizations, and suppliers such as feed companies. Many analysts have pointed up the magnitude of the
agricultural credit needs in the future, but few concrete suggestions have been put forth as to how these credit needs can
best be met. There has been an implicit assumption that for
the most part the future needs can be met through proper adjustments in the policies of present lenders—both private and

public. It may be, however, that wholly new agencies or systems will be called for to solve the problem adequately.

Regardless of the sources of credit and capital, those firms believed to have greater potential for success will find it somewhat easier to obtain the needed funds. Others will find various degrees of restriction imposed with the loans. These restrictions may be only liens on the property to assure repayment or they may be more formalized contracts calling for the creditor to assist in management, to sell the products, or to provide other services.

Extension of Managerial Capacity

As the size of the unit expands, some producers will reach the upper limit of their managerial capacity. Many producers will be able to extend this limit through the use of information gained from formal or informal educational programs, and the experiences or observations of others. Some producers may in effect extend the limits of their managerial capacity by hiring managers. However, many producers probably will not avail themselves of managerial services until it is too late for such services to benefit them. Managerial capacity will be extended rather rapidly over the years ahead through the use of education and information and the hiring of professional management advice through some type of contract arrangement.

Increased Attention to Marketing Problems

Even though the average size of livestock production units is expected to grow rapidly between the late 1950's and 1975, such units will still be much smaller in volume than most meat packers and processors and retail meat buying operations. The individual producer may therefore be placed at a disadvantage as far as relative bargaining power over the sale of his product is concerned. As producing units become relatively larger and better informed with respect to the marketing of their products, their relative bargaining strength in the marketplace will tend to increase. At the same time, however, the market influence of other segments of the industry such as food retailing, will probably increase even more. Individual producers as a whole are likely to experience a net loss in relative bargaining power. The growing inequality in bargaining or market power will increase the producer's interest in the marketing of his product. Individual producers, producer groups, or others may attempt to achieve a larger measure of market power through control of a large volume of their product, differentiation of their product, control over supply, or other means.

Producer Marketing Alternatives

There are a number of courses of action that livestock producers may take under the circumstances just described. These courses of action are neither all-inclusive nor mutually exclusive. Only the seemingly more important alternatives are discussed here.

Selling by the Producer

In the past most producers decided upon the kind and amount of livestock to produce and the time of sale. Under this system of marketing, the individual producer interpreted the market and decided how he could best use the resources at his command to satisfy the market demand. In the future, marketing may continue to be conducted in this way. Sales may be accomplished on a bargaining basis, or through a terminal market or auction. There may be an informal agreement or a contract arrangement between the producer and the buyer. The producer would, however, carry primary responsibility in deciding what was produced and when the product was sold.

This kind of marketing system has the advantage of affording producers a maximum amount of freedom in production and marketing decisions. Its disadvantages seem to be instability in production, prices, and incomes and a failure to provide either the more uniform qualities or quantities desired by the operators of marketing agencies and consumers.

Selling Through Marketing Organizations

One alternative open to producers is to assign the marketing function to a marketing firm. This could be either a private or a cooperative organization. To be effective, such an organization would need the support of its members in order to exercise the necessary control over the kind, quality, and timing of livestock produced. The organization would probably find it necessary to help in financing, management, providing breeding stock, and feeding. A formal contract between the marketing organization and the producer undoubtedly would be required.

For most producers the marketing organization alternative seems to offer several advantages. Production and marketing could be programmed more in line with market demand. The organization personnel could be in touch with a wider variety of markets than the individual producers. The disadvantages of marketing organizations would be the difficulty of acquiring skilled management and marketing personnel. There is also the possibility that the market will not reflect enough premium to cover the extra costs of the service demanded. To some extent, however, this will depend upon the bargaining power and ability of the organizations' personnel.

The functions to be performed by marketing organizations need to be delineated carefully. It is one job to market livestock to the best possible advantage, given the general economic framework. It is another matter to change the general level of livestock prices through government or private-group action. While the two jobs are interrelated, it seems doubtful that the same organization can do both well.

The strictly marketing organizations might find it wise to

limit membership or patronage to those producers of a certain size—the larger producers, perhaps—whose products are a specific quality that fits the organization needs. It may be easier for a private organization to limit membership or patronage than for a cooperative organization to do the same thing. Such limitations might be regarded as violations of the basic principles of cooperation. If the organizers or members of the organization impose such restrictions upon themselves, there would seem to be less question about the validity of the restrictions. In any case, such restrictions on membership or patronage seem to be warranted in helping assure the success of the organization. Such a marketing organization would have interests in policy decisions regarding price support operations by government or private-group actions designed to affect price levels, but its primary function would be marketing.

The activities concerned with affecting the general level of livestock and meat prices and the framework under which these are determined could be assumed by a separate organization of producers. Since most of the members of such an organization would probably be producers desiring an increase in price and income, the group would probably be most concerned with this problem. As many producers feel differently toward government agricultural policies, such an organization would have difficulty in obtaining agreement from its members on the kind of program to follow. Such opportunities for disagreement would make it desirable for a marketing organization to stick as closely as possible to marketing and try to avoid agricultural policy disputes.

Producer-members or patrons and management of livestock marketing organizations may become interested in processing their own meat and establishing their own retail outlets. Forward integration of this type poses many problems. Large amounts of capital would be required for facilities, and possession of the facilities does not necessarily assure a market for the livestock and meat.

Increased Contract or Prearranged Selling

Marketing agencies, meat packers and processors, and possibly retail stores will be seeking ways to assure quantity and quality of product at the time desired. Feed companies or other suppliers will make an effort to increase the sale of their products. This effort will include the extension of credit, management assistance, and other services. At least one or all of these groups will be interested in making formal or informal agreements that will serve their purposes. While these contracts or agreements initially will be more prevalent with hogs, the idea will also be extended to cattle at a later date. In 1958 between 5% and 10% of all hogs were produced under some type of production and marketing contract.[33] The comparable percentage estimate of cattle produced under contract is somewhat lower. It does not include, however, the large numbers of cattle that are fed under contract with commercial feedlots.

In most cases the incentive for producers to sign formal contracts will be to gain access to added capital or credit at an apparently reasonable rate and, for some producers, to take advantage of the management services offered. Others, however, will sign contracts or make informal arrangements primarily as a means of shedding the marketing responsibility so they can concentrate on production. In general producers will have to be shown that they will receive more positive advantages before they will make informal or formal arrangements with marketing agencies.

There is the possibility that once these arrangements become widespread so that they cover a substantial portion of the market, the nonconformist may find a poorer market for his product. If a high percentage of the livestock produced is sold on a contract basis, the volume of receipts at terminal markets and auctions will fall appreciably. Such markets may

[33] Correspondence with R. C. Kramer, Michigan State University, East Lansing, Michigan.

then become a less desirable place to market noncontract livestock. If, however, there are nonconformists among the buyers who prefer to resist the development of production contracts, the producers who shy away from contracts or similar arrangements may reap the gains, at least in the short run.

Many people in agriculture are concerned about the consequences of the movement toward contract farming and vertical integration. The loss of individual freedom to make management decisions is cited as one of the main undesirable consequences of vertical integration. The extent of the limitations on the producer's freedom depends upon the conditions written into the contract. Research and study on the various types of contracts are urgently needed so that the likely consequences to both parties can be assessed properly.

Loss of individual freedom of management by the producer is one of the by-products of contracting for the production and marketing of livestock. The producer must take this factor into account in deciding whether the advantages of signing a contract outweigh the disadvantages. The typical livestock production contract in use in 1958 puts a minimum of restrictions on the managerial freedom of the individual producer. The principal fear of those who are suspicious of producer contracts and integration is that agriculture may become an industry of hired laborers rather than owner-operators. This could happen if the production units passed out of the control of individual farmers. While there will undoubtedly be increases in output produced by these integrated kinds of units, the bulk of livestock production will still come from individually owned units or units owned and operated by the owners. The effect of the producer contract may, in fact, be to preserve this kind of ownership rather than displace it. A successfully operated contract system of production will reduce the need for marketing organizations, feed companies, meat packers and processors, and retail food stores to own livestock production units on a large scale.

Chapter VIII

INSTABILITY IN THE LIVESTOCK AND MEAT ECONOMY

AMONG THE forces working toward change in both the horizontal and the vertical structure of the meat economy is the instability of production, prices, and income. The instability problem of the livestock and meat economy is composed of at least two separate, yet closely related, problem areas. One is the level of prices and income in comparison with other agricultural and nonagricultural enterprises over extended periods of time. The second general problem area concerns the variability or instability of livestock production and prices and the consequent variability in income over relatively short periods of time. The income level problem of livestock producers is closely interrelated with the price and income problems of agriculture in general. Since detailed analysis of income levels for agriculture goes well beyond the scope of this report, our attention will be centered here on the shorter run variations in livestock production, price, and income.

The demand for meat is relatively stable, both within the year and from year to year. On the other hand, the production of livestock in total and by species varies considerably during the year and from year to year. The net result is instability in livestock and meat prices. The kinds, qualities, and quantities of meat and meat products moving through the marketing channels also are continually changing. The instability in quantities and prices of livestock and meat affects firms and individuals at all stages of the marketing process in a variety of ways. A few firms or individuals can adjust readily to the variations in supplies and prices of livestock and meat with little effect on their operations or profit position. For most firms and individuals involved in the marketing of meat, however, the instability of supplies and prices results in instability in income. In general, the variations in livestock production are of two types. One is the longer run cyclical variations in numbers—particularly for cattle and hogs. The other is the variation in numbers that occurs during the year, largely as a result of seasonal bunching of animal births.

Cycles in Production

The long-time trend in livestock numbers has been upward. Such an upward movement in numbers would be expected in line with changes in population, income, and other factors associated with demand for the products. The patterns of change in livestock numbers over the years have not been smooth. There seems to be a cyclical movement in production and prices for both cattle and hogs but not for sheep and lambs. One explanation of the cycles in livestock production is referred to as the "cobweb theorem," [1] which holds that adjustments in production in response to price changes are in effect overdone. The producer has imperfect knowledge regarding future prices; there is a tendency for production decisions to be influenced more heavily by current than by future prices, and for each producer to ignore the effect that his own production will have on prices. Therefore, if current prices appear favorable, producers start building up breeding stock in order to capitalize on what seems to be a favorable market.

Keeping breeding stock off the market reduces the market supply of livestock, and livestock prices may rise above already favorable levels. At a later date when the offspring of the retained breeding stock, plus the normal flow of animals, come

[1] M. J. B. Ezekiel, "The Cobweb Theorem," *Quarterly Journal of Economics*, February 1938, 52:255.

Figure 6

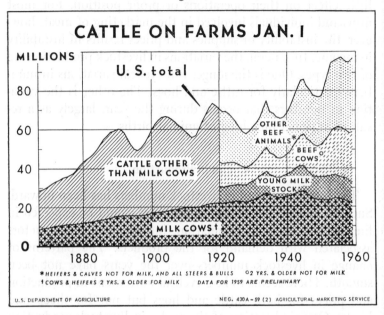

CATTLE ON FARMS JAN. I

MILLIONS

U. S. total

80

60   OTHER
        BEEF
        ANIMALS*

40   CATTLE OTHER   BEEF
      THAN MILK COWS   COWS

                                YOUNG MILK
                                STOCK

20

              MILK COWS†

0
      1880   1900   1920   1940   1960

*HEIFERS & CALVES NOT FOR MILK, AND ALL STEERS & BULLS   ◦2 YRS. & OLDER NOT FOR MILK
†COWS & HEIFERS 2 YRS. & OLDER FOR MILK   DATA FOR 1959 ARE PRELIMINARY

U.S. DEPARTMENT OF AGRICULTURE   NEG. 430A–59 (2) AGRICULTURAL MARKETING SERVICE

to market, prices fall. At this point prices become unfavorable instead of favorable. Future production is discouraged by the unfavorable market and the breeding stock is sent to market, further depressing the livestock prices. The reduction in numbers proceeds to a point where livestock supply becomes relatively short and prices again appear favorable for producers. The stage is thus set for another increase in numbers.

Cattle

The historical cycle in cattle numbers is pronounced and fairly regular (Figure 6). Three trend periods can be distinguished: (1) the rapid expansion of the cattle industry up to the 1880's; (2) the period of slower growth rate from the 1880's through the 1920's; and (3) the period since the 1920's,

Figure 7

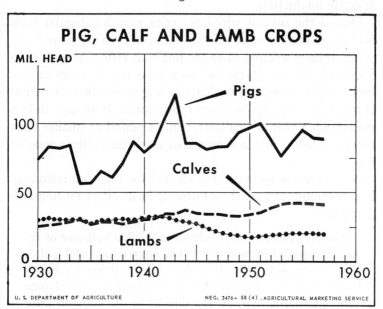

PIG, CALF AND LAMB CROPS

MIL. HEAD

Pigs

100

Calves

50

Lambs

0

1930   1940   1950   1960

U. S. DEPARTMENT OF AGRICULTURE   NEG. 3476– 58 (4) . AGRICULTURAL MARKETING SERVICE

which has shown a more rapid rate of growth and shorter cycles (i.e., 10 to 12 years in length).[2]

Hogs

The total number of pigs saved per year rose slowly during the period 1930–1959 (Figure 7). Calculated on an annual basis pig production seemed to follow a fairly regular four- to six-year cyclical pattern. One cycle started in 1948, when hog numbers began increasing, and ended in 1953, when another upturn began. The cycle beginning in 1953 had apparently run its course by 1956–1957. The cycles in pig production

[2] This material on cycles in cattle and hog production is adapted from R. C. Kramer, R. A. Goldberg, and J. H. Davis, "An Agribusiness Appraisal of the Meat Economy," unpublished manuscript, Division of Research, Harvard Business School, Boston, Massachusetts, May 1957.

seem less uniform in length and in magnitude than the cycles in cattle production.

One of the reasons why hog cycles were less regular than beef cycles was the close relation between corn prices and hog prices, usually referred to as the hog-corn ratio.[3] According to Shepherd, changes in the hog-corn ratio are the main factors back of the cyclical movements in hog production. A period of larger than average hog-corn ratios causes an increase in hog marketings a year or two later, while a period of smaller than average ratios causes a decrease in marketing after a year or two.[4]

A more recent analysis suggests that the hog-corn ratio may be less important now than formerly in its effect on hog production.

> The hog-corn ratio formerly was a reliable indicator of future changes in hog production. The ratio, though still useful, is a less accurate indication than before. Being no longer linked so closely with corn, hog production is freer to change "on its own." It responds less directly to the hog-corn price ratio than previously, and there is some tendency for under-response and over-response to appear alternately.[5]

Regardless of the cause of cycles in livestock production and prices, it seems clear that such cycles are an evidence of imperfection in the operation of the market over periods of time. They cause alternate periods of overcrowding and underutilization of production equipment, thereby increasing costs.[6]

Other agencies in the marketing chain also feel the impact of cycles in livestock production and marketing. The number of animals handled by marketing agencies varies according to

---

[3] The hog-corn ratio expresses the relationship between hog prices and corn prices. If hogs are selling at $20 per cwt. and corn is $1.00 per bushel, the hog-corn ratio would be 20:1 or 20.

[4] Geoffrey S. Shepherd, *Marketing Farm Products* (Ames, Iowa, Iowa State College Press, 3rd ed., 1955), pp. 124–126.

[5] *The Livestock and Meat Situation*, May 1958, pp. 17 and 18.

[6] Shepherd, *Marketing Farm Products*, pp. 128–129.

the stage in the production cycle. Slaughterers must maintain adequate facilities to handle peak loads, which means that they have considerable unused plant capacities at other times. Cyclical changes in types and qualities of animals also mean that slaughterers must adapt their merchandising operations to handle different qualities and types of meat. Variations in the number of breeding stock being sent to the market affect the composition of the meat supply, which means that wholesalers and retailers feel the impact in terms of differences in the price and availability of certain cuts or qualities of meat.

Seasonality in Livestock Marketing, Slaughter, and Prices [7]

The production and marketing of most species of livestock follow a fairly regular seasonal pattern. The meat supply is usually largest in the fall and winter and smallest in the spring and summer. A large part of the seasonal variation results from the seasonal bunching of animal births. The fact that the grazing season ends at about the same time in most regions also helps to crowd marketing into a single period. Weather conditions and the need for fitting the livestock enterprises into the over-all farm business also contribute to the seasonal swings in livestock production. Since the demand for products is relatively stable, livestock prices vary inversely in response to the seasonal changes in production.

Cattle

The normal seasonal variation in receipts of cattle at public stockyards during the 1947–1953 period ranged from a low of 22% below the annual average in February to a high of 45% above the annual average in October. The seasonal variation in the number of cattle slaughtered is smaller than the varia-

---

[7] See U. S. Agricultural Marketing Service, Agriculture Handbook No. 83, "Charting the Seasonal Market for Meat Animals," by Harold Breimyer and Charlotte A. Kause (Washington, Government Printing Office, June 1955).

tion in receipts of all live animals. The more uniform supply of cattle results from feedlot operations. Cattle are put on feed in greatest numbers at the end of the grazing season. Seasonally concentrated marketing of grass cattle is thereby transformed into a more evenly distributed supply of slaughter cattle of higher grade and weight.

The comparatively constant year-long supply of fed cattle is made up of a shifting composition of grades. At Chicago, choice and prime steers were only 57% of the total in February but 82% in July, August, and September during the 1947–1953 period.

Cattle prices reached their seasonal peak in May and June when they averaged about 4% or 5% above the annual average. The low point in cattle prices during the season was in November and December when prices averaged 5% below the average for the year. The various grades of cattle had different seasonal price patterns depending upon relative supplies of grades being marketed at any one time. The seasonal variation in the prices for calves was similar to cattle during the 1947–1953 period, but calves reached their price peak in February.

Hogs

The seasonal variation in hog marketing was somewhat different from the variations in cattle marketing. Hog farrowings are bunched at two times during the year—in spring and fall. During the 1947–1953 period the marketing peak for spring pigs occurred from October to January with a peak of 33% above the annual average. This figure is much higher than the marketing peak for fall pigs, which occurred during the March–May period. The low point in hog marketings during the 1947–1953 period occurred in July and August and was 22% below the annual average.

Hogs are not adapted to extended feeding beyond a preferred market weight. At heavier weights, their grade and therefore their price is usually reduced. The seasonal path of hog slaughter is then virtually the same as that of production and marketing. Seasonal swings in the slaughter of barrows and gilts are even more pronounced than those of total hog slaughter since producers customarily market many sows after spring farrowing. By farrowing earlier in the year, feeding for faster gain, and achieving more nearly equal balance between fall and spring pig crops, producers have reduced slightly the seasonal variation in hog marketings and slaughter over the last 30 years. Slaughter in September, October and November has increased more than the slaughter in February, May, June, and July.

The seasonal variation in hog prices during the 1947–1953 period was somewhat greater than the average seasonal variation in prices of other species and kinds of livestock. Hog prices reached one peak in September with another, lower peak in March. The low point in prices during the season usually occurred in November or December. The prices during the 1947–1953 period averaged between a high of about 9% above the annual average to 9% below the average.

Sheep and Lambs

Sheep and lamb receipts at public stockyards during the 1947–1953 period in October averaged 57% above the annual average. The average for September was nearly as high. The low point in marketing occurred in February and March when receipts were about 25% below the annual average. Sheep and lambs marketed direct to packers or feeder-buyers are not included in the statistics. Since these marketings are highly concentrated in the fall months, the seasonal peaks in total marketings are probably more pronounced than those reported for public markets alone. As a result of feeding operations, the variation in sheep and lamb slaughter is not as great as the seasonal variation in marketings. These feeding operations tend to even out the supply of lambs for slaughter during the year.

Lamb prices are usually highest during the months of April, May, and June and lowest in the fall, when marketings are at their peak. The prices of sheep reach their peak in April and are at their low point in the late fall.

Total Meat Supply

The seasonal meat supply is not so variable as the oscillations in livestock marketings would indicate. Most of the changes in commercial meat production throughout the season can be related to changes or fluctuations in hog production.

For all meats combined the maximum seasonal variations in production in the 1947–1953 period ranged between a 15% excess over average monthly output in December and a 10% deficit in July. As would be expected, meat is placed in cold storage in winter for sale in summer. Storage of pork accounted for about three-fourths of all meat stored during the 1947–1953 period. The peak in storage occurred about March 1 and usually equaled about 6% of the year's total pork supply. Low point in pork storage was usually around November 1.

Most beef put in storage was cow beef held to be sold as ground beef and other processed products during the summer. Beef storage stocks were ordinarily at peak volume on February 1, with approximately 2% of the year's production in storage.

Wholesale and Retail Price Variations

During the 1947–1953 period wholesale and retail prices of meat followed the same general seasonal pattern as prices of comparable species of livestock. In general, wholesale meat prices varied somewhat less than livestock prices, and retail meat prices varied even less. Both wholesale and retail meat prices include charges for services as well as for the product itself. Since the costs of the services are slower to change than the prices or costs of the product, wholesale and retail prices show relatively greater stability than livestock prices. The storage of meat during periods of peak supply and the later movement of this meat to the consumer also helps to damp the seasonal swings in wholesale and retail meat prices.

Variability in Producer Income

The effect of the instability in livestock production and prices on net farm income is not easily isolated. Other factors, such as the general level of prices, the weather, and government programs, which are changing concurrently also affect producer income. There is no question, however, that the sizable variations over short periods of time in the income of livestock producers result in part from the instability in livestock production and prices.

Data for the various types of farms in the Corn Belt show that while, in general, incomes have tended to rise since 1940, the path has not been smooth (Figure 8). Changes of 20% to 30% in income in both directions from one year to the next are not uncommon for most farming areas. Somewhat larger changes from year to year may be common in areas where the production is quite variable because of weather conditions. Compared with most other industries and types of employment, agriculture in general and livestock producers in particular have highly variable net incomes.

There is great variation in returns among the various types of farming areas expressed on a per hour basis.[8] The returns per hour of labor vary quite widely from year to year, primarily as a result of income fluctuations, since numbers of hours worked tend to be constant.

[8] See Appendix Table 34 for more detail on returns per hour in selected types of farming areas, 1947–1949, 1954–1957.

Figure 8

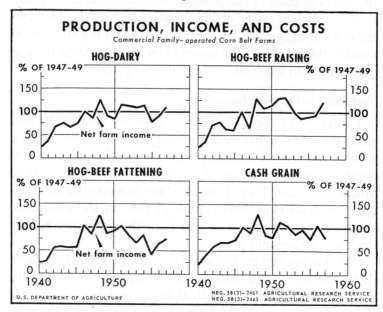

PRODUCTION, INCOME, AND COSTS
Commercial Family– operated Corn Belt Farms

U. S. DEPARTMENT OF AGRICULTURE

NEG. 58(3)– 2461 AGRICULTURAL RESEARCH SERVICE
NEG. 58(3)– 2462 AGRICULTURAL RESEARCH SERVICE

Income Variability in Other Segments

Incomes of segments of the livestock and meat industry other than producers also vary from year to year. The packing industry, for example, recorded earnings of 1.5% of sales in 1947 but only 0.4% in 1954 (Table 23). Similarly the earnings per 100 pounds of dressed weight in 1954 were only about one-fourth as much as they were in 1947. Changes of 50% to 100% in rate of earnings from year to year are not uncommon. While there are many reasons for the variability in earnings, one of the major factors is the variability in livestock supplies and prices.

The influence of volume on the costs of operations of livestock auctions, dealer markets, and other marketing agencies has already been noted. In general, the relatively high fixed

Table 23. Earnings as a Percentage of Total Sales and Net Worth, and Earnings per 100 Pounds of Live and Dressed Weight for the Meat Packing Industry, 1947–1957

	Earnings as a Percentage of		Earnings per 100 lbs.* of	
Year	Total Sales	Net Worth	Live Weight	Dressed Weight
1957	.7%	5.5%	$.19	$.30
1956	1.0	8.4	.26	.41
1955	.9	8.1	.25	.40
1954	.4	3.6	.13	.20
1953	.8	6.7	.24	.37
1952	.5	4.4	.16	.25
1951	.7	6.9	.26	.40
1950	.9	7.7	.28	.43
1949	.6	5.7	.19	.31
1948	.9	9.2	.31	.50
1947	1.5	15.3	.45	.74

* Earnings are overstated to the extent that they are derived from non-meat operations.

Source: Calculated from *Financial Facts About the Meat Packing Industry, 1957* (Chicago, American Meat Institute, July 1958), p. 24.

costs and the excess capacity of many organizations mean that for most firms reductions in supplies result in higher operating costs per unit handled.

Reducing Instability

Several suggestions have been made for reducing the instability problem of livestock production and prices. One suggestion is that research and education be improved. The theory is that better information, more skillfully utilized, would reduce the magnitude of the fluctuation in livestock numbers. A second suggestion, closely related to the first, is that multiple farrowings of hogs be stressed. Farrowings would then be more regular throughout the year and thus reduce the seasonal swings in production and prices. A third suggestion is that producer contracts be advocated as a stabilization measure. The contracts would call for a specified number of animals of a specified kind or quality to be delivered at a specified date.

Some producers and producer leaders have expressed the opinion that the answer would be for the producers to market their livestock through a marketing organization. Such an organization would handle a high percentage of the livestock production either over a wide geographical area or over the entire country. While the primary function of such an organization might be to increase bargaining power and thus influence prices received, it might also conceivably be in a position to stabilize production. Lastly, there are those who say that if the industry is to become more stable, the government will have to take some kind of action. But there is no agreement as to what the government's role ought to be.

Improving Research and Education

In making plans for the future, the producer must have some idea of the price he expects. Current prices or prices in the immediate past greatly influence the price expectations of livestock producers. If prices of one commodity appear relatively good, production of this commodity is expanded. Conversely, if price relations for a similar commodity are unfavorable, production is curtailed. The decisions made by individual producers on this basis combine to create the instability of livestock production. If this instability is to be reduced, producers need more accurate estimates of future price relations than those currently in use.

The United States Department of Agriculture and the various land grant colleges conduct research and extension work designed to give producers better information and tools to use in analyzing or predicting the future. Some organizations that sell livestock for producers or buy from producers also supply and analyze market information for their members or patrons. Practically every farm magazine carries a market page with an analysis of the current situation and sometimes a prediction of things to come. Private management letters or "tip sheets" for agriculture frequently devote pages or whole issues to the outlook for farm commodities. The market news service of the United States Department of Agriculture, the Departments of Agriculture of the various states, and many private sources collect and disseminate current market news on agricultural products.

The instability in livestock production and prices has continued in spite of rather extensive research and educational efforts designed to reduce it. This is not a criticism of the so-called outlook and market information work. The continued instability in production probably reflects a lack of resources devoted to these projects—to research particularly. In many cases there is not enough of the right kind of information available to permit accurate forecasts of the future. Data on what has happened in the past is not enough. The data must be submitted to a sufficiently dynamic analysis to make possible the estimation of prices when several variables are changing concurrently. The use of electronic computers and the appropriate statistical techniques now enable researchers to handle and analyze data and solve problems that were very formidable just a few years ago. It seems likely that the application of modern research techniques will improve the accuracy of outlook predictions.

Multiple Farrowings

The seasonal variation in hog prices results largely from seasonal variations in marketings, which in turn is directly related to the bunching of sow farrowings at two seasons of the year. This leads directly to the proposition that if farrowings were distributed more evenly throughout the year, marketings would be more even and hence prices would be more stable. The advocates of multiple farrowing present many arguments in its favor. One of the major points in favor of such a system is the greater use that can be made of fairly expensive facilities. In addition, multiple farrowing is said to result in the use of better breeding stock to allow for better labor balance, and to provide a year-round income. Such a production system should reduce speculation, lessen disease risk, and keep the consumer in the pork-buying habit.[9] One large meat packing company recently set up a demonstration farm designed among other things to show midwestern producers how to produce hogs efficiently with multiple farrowing.

Land grant colleges and Department of Agriculture research and extension personnel have not given unqualified endorsement to multiple farrowing. The advantages are recognized, but some important limitations are also pointed out. The question has been raised, for example, as to whether the labor requirements of multiple farrowing can be successfully meshed with labor requirements of other enterprises in a general crop and livestock farm. In addition, many livestock producers may not have the managerial capacity needed to operate a multiple farrowing system successfully. The average sales price of hogs produced under a multiple farrowing system may be lower since hogs are sold at all seasons rather than during periods of high seasonal prices. In addition, some research has indicated that cost savings for multiple farrowing are rather small.[10]

The United States Department of Agriculture and several state experiment stations have projects under way to determine the advantages and disadvantages of multiple farrowing. If managerial capacity is a limiting factor in the development of multiple farrowing systems, the adoption of these systems ought to speed up, since it is expected that the fewer larger producers of the future will have a much higher level of man-

[9] Lewis Reeve et al., More Swine Dollars from Multiple Farrowing (Chicago, American Meat Institute, 1957), pp. 4–6.

[10] Ronald Bauman, "Comparable Costs of Portable and Permanent Structures in Swine Production and the Effect of Intensity of Use on Costs," Some Considerations in Intensified Systems of Hog Production, Mimeo ID-19, Purdue University, April 17, 1957, p. 30.

agement ability. The advent of widespread use of contracts in the production of hogs could also result in rapid adoption of multiple farrowing systems. This would be especially true if the contracts call for management assistance for the producer and contain provisions governing the time of sale of the animals.

Producer Contracts

Producer contracts have often been advocated as a stabilizing device for the industry, the assumption being that if a high percentage of the output were produced under contract, the decision making would be centralized. Such centralized decision makers are supposed to be in a better position to estimate future market demand and price than a large number of individual producers making decisions on an individual basis.

Experience in the broiler industry suggests that this will be true only if the decision making is confined to relatively few centers. Even though the number of decision-making centers in broiler production has been lowered greatly in recent years, the almost chaotic supply and price conditions existing in 1958–1959 suggest that the concentration has not gone far enough to give real stability to the industry. The likelihood that the livestock and meat industry will be so organized that the decisions regarding production are made by few enough units to achieve stability in production and price seems remote, for the aggregations of capital needed to finance and operate such units in livestock production would be extremely large.

The concentration of decision making in fewer and fewer hands may lead to more instability than stability. Each decision-making unit is larger under a centralized system, but such units still must make decisions with imperfect knowledge as to what their competitors are going to do. If they all move in the same direction, the swings in production and price may be amplified instead of reduced. Widespread use of producer contracts will probably be more effective in reducing the instability of production and prices within the year than from year to year. The effect of such a development on cyclical variation in price and production will depend upon the contractor's skill in estimating future supplies and demands. If such contractors are more skillful than individual producers in estimating future supplies, demands, and prices, the use of contracts might have a stabilizing effect on cyclical variations in livestock production. If the experience in broiler production can be used as a guide, there would seem to be little reason to suspect that a system of livestock production under contract would greatly alleviate the cyclical instability problem in livestock production.

Few Large Marketing Organizations

It is often suggested that if a very large organization had control over a high percentage of the livestock marketed, the industry could be stabilized. Such a situation has long been the dream of many farm and cooperative leaders. Although livestock marketing organizations will become fewer in number and larger in size between 1959 and 1975, the chances seem remote that such organizations will have effective control of the supply of livestock in total or the production of particular species for any great length of time. Plans designed to control or regulate production would probably be unworkable without some assistance from the government in the form of legislation and enforcement. This is not to say that the idea of controlling supply is necessarily bad or unworkable. The point is that private groups operating in the competitive framework existing in agriculture have found it difficult if not impossible to control production and raise prices without outside help.

Government Programs

The present and proposed direct action by government falls under two broad headings. One set of programs is designed to make the production and marketing of livestock more stable. The other programs are primarily designed to maintain or raise the general level of prices and incomes of livestock producers. Income is a more meaningful concept than price alone since income depends not only on price but also upon quantity produced and sold and the costs of performing these functions. Many suggested government programs, of course, are designed to cover both of the above objectives—increased stability and higher prices and incomes. There are three chief disadvantages to government stability programs: (1) the cost of the program either in consumer prices or in taxes, (2) the difficulty of controlling production and enforcing the restrictions, (3) the problems of finding a market outlet if the price is above the normal market price.

Income Payments. One plan that has been suggested as a means of stabilizing the livestock industry hinges around the use of income payments to hog producers when prices move below certain specified levels.[11] These payments would keep producers from cutting back as drastically in production as they might otherwise do when prices begin to fall. This would in turn supposedly reduce the magnitude of the following upswing in price and hence make the industry more stable. This plan contemplates stabilization action on a fairly large scale by the Commodity Credit Corporation of the U. S. Department of Agriculture. Presumably administrators of the Congressional program would determine the level of prices at which income payments would be made. If the purpose of the plan were only stabilization, the point at which income payments would start would probably be lower than if the plan were designed to support prices and incomes.

A further refinement that could be added to this kind of plan would be to make the income payments only for hogs

[11] M. R. Benedict, "Current Imbalance of Supply and Demand for Farm Products," in U. S. Congress, Subcommittee on Agricultural Policy, Joint Economic Committee, *The Policy for Commercial Agriculture, Its Relation to Economic Growth and Stability,* 85th Cong., 1st Sess., November 22, 1957, pp. 91–107.

meeting certain standards. For example, paying only on hogs grading No. 1 and weighing less than 225 pounds might help speed up the shift to meat type hogs and also help cut the total weight of animals marketed. Thus, the payments would be used to improve the quality of hogs produced and marketed. These qualifications could be set up so that the resulting consumer product contained less fat and was otherwise more desirable.

The stabilization of prices and income of livestock producers through the use of income payments has all the disadvantages of any kind of direct payment price support proposal. Direct payments carry more of a connotation of subsidy or dole than other ways of putting government funds into the farmer's hands. There is also a chance that direct payments may become costly to the U. S. Treasury, particularly if the support price is placed at relatively high levels. Producers may not understand the relation between the income payments and hog prices since the two would be received at different times during the year. If so, the production decisions might not be altered appreciably by this type of income supplement and there would be little improvement in stability of the industry.

On the other hand, if such payments at a moderate level could bring a greater degree of stability to the industry, the gains to the industry and to society in general might be more than the costs to the U. S. Treasury. Prices paid producers for livestock would not go as low under a system of direct payment as they might if such a program were not in effect. If the direct payments are an effective stabilization measure, prices will not go as high as they would without the direct payments. A direct payment program has another advantage in that the consumer gets the benefit of lower prices if supplies reduce producer prices to below the support level. This is in contrast with programs calling for buying and storage of products by the government where consumer prices generally reflect the price-raising actions taken by the government.

Direct Purchases. While there has been no formal price support program for meat products, the government has at times purchased meat products to bolster the market.[12] These purchases were made primarily for use in school lunch programs and relief feeding at home and abroad. In recent years some products have been exported under Public Law 480 programs where the products are paid for in local foreign currencies.[13] Until now the amounts of meat products purchased by the government under any of these programs have been only a small percentage of total production of meat.

It would be possible for the government to expand the direct buying programs as a stabilization measure. It could be operated much like the income payment method just outlined except that purchases of products would be made in the market place to keep the prices from going to what seemed to be unduly low levels. The meat products accumulated under a purchase-type price support program could be disposed of through the same channels as have been used to dispose of the limited quantities of government meat purchases in the past.

Government purchases of meat products would keep livestock prices from going as low as they might if prices were not supported. This reduction in price variability would keep producers from cutting back on hog and beef production as far as they otherwise might. And the likelihood of later cyclical overexpansion would be decreased.

A direct purchase program would encounter the same difficulties as the income support plan in determining the price level at which the plan should become operative. Experience in other commodities indicates that it is sometimes easy to accumulate relatively large quantities of surplus products that are sometimes difficult even to give away. Any large-scale government purchase program faces the difficulty of moving the

---

[12] See Appendix Table 35 for detail breakdown of government purchases of surplus meat and lard, 1951–1958.

[13] See Appendix Table 36 for exports under P.L. 480.

government-owned products into consumption without replacing in total or in part the products in normal trade channels. Quite often this means that the government-owned products have to be given away or sold at a very low price. This, of course, represents a cost to the federal government. Storage of products, particularly perishables, is also relatively expensive.

If the purchase program is designed to support prices for prolonged periods of time above levels that would otherwise have existed in the market, some kind of production control would have to be included in the program. Such controls over production would be necessary in order to keep the cost of the program at what seems to be a "reasonable" level.[14] In general, the higher that prices are maintained compared with what they would have been without the purchase program, the greater will be the need for production controls. Thus far agricultural production control by the government has not been very successful, but perhaps controls could be devised for livestock that would be more effective. A price stabilization program with effective control might, however, be unacceptable to a majority of producers. Individual producers would have to decide for themselves whether the advantages of such a plan outweighted the disadvantages. In the past, production control programs have been instituted only after a favorable vote by producers.

Livestock producers and their representatives have prided themselves on being one of the remaining strongholds of freedom from government price supports, purchase programs, and controls of agriculture. This philosophy was sorely tested during the period of low prices in the fall of 1955. At that time many industry leaders sounded the call for increased government help. In view of the relatively large supplies of livestock and meat expected during the next few years, price and income

---

[14] What is reasonable to one group such as producers may be entirely unreasonable to another group. In the final analysis Congress will have to decide which programs are or are not reasonable in cost.

relations for livestock producers are again expected to be somewhat less favorable. This development will bring with it a renewed clamor for government aid.

Marketing Orders. Another stabilization proposal that has been put forward is the application of the marketing order or agreement concept to meat products. The legislation under which marketing orders and agreements operate is very specific as to what commodities can be covered.[15] Since meat products are not on the list, new or amended legislation would be required if such a marketing plan were to be applied to meat. In the 1950's the turkey industry was interested in the possibility of using marketing orders. Developments there may show the advantages and pitfalls of such plans in the marketing of a livestock product.

Marketing orders can be instituted for a variety of purposes. They might be used to provide a mechanism for collecting funds to be used for advertising and promoting a product. They might specify the qualities or quantities of product that could be shipped from a particular area. Or they might be used in an attempt to establish minimum prices to be paid producers for various kinds and qualities of livestock. The provisions written into the order would of course vary according to the purpose of the order. Marketing orders are promulgated after testimony is presented at public hearings. All interested parties have an opportunity to present testimony in favor of or against complete orders or particular sections of them. Marketing orders must be voted on favorably by a certain percentage of producers before becoming effective. Similarly a negative producer vote cancels the operation of the marketing order. Once in operation the marketing orders carry the weight of federal law behind them and the provisions can be enforced through federal courts. Even though everyone involved in the marketing of the

[15] For a more complete discussion of marketing orders and agreements see "Farmer in a Changing World," *Yearbook of Agriculture, 1940,* pp. 641–649, and "Marketing," *Yearbook of Agriculture, 1954,* pp. 357–363.

product does not agree with the desirability or features of the marketing order, all must obey the regulations once the order is issued and the prescribed percentage of producers vote in favor of it.

While it has been suggested that marketing orders be used to regulate the sale of livestock, few if any specific proposals for inclusion in such orders have been formulated. The scattered location of livestock production, irregularity of marketing, lack of standardized quality, large numbers of species and different kinds of animals, and the fact that not all animals are sold for slaughter make it extremely difficult to establish a workable marketing order plan that would make livestock marketing more stable.

A marketing order might set up the machining whereby a portion of the supply of various kinds or species of livestock could be diverted from normal market channels during periods of abnormally great supply. This action would be designed to keep producer prices from falling as low as they otherwise would and thus would make future production more stable. Such a marketing order would establish a scale of minimum prices to be paid for livestock slaughtered and sold as fresh or processed meats. Another scale of prices would be established for livestock diverted from normal trade channels. Such diversion of product would be necessary if the prices paid by the slaughterers and processors under the terms of the marketing order resulted in greater production than could be sold at consumer prices resulting from the order prices plus processing and marketing charges. The amount of products to be diverted would depend upon the producer prices set under the order. If the object of the marketing order is only stability of production and price, the order price will be somewhat lower than if the objective is to stabilize producer prices at a somewhat higher level, thereby increasing producer income. If stability is the goal, diversion of product would be limited to times of peak cyclical or seasonal production. If increasing prices and incomes is the goal of the marketing order, diversion of product would be a more nearly continuous operation.

The diverted products could be utilized in the same way as other surplus agricultural products, e.g., in the school lunch programs and domestic and foreign rehabilitation and relief activities. It is conceivable that the diverted products could be processed into tankage or some other nonfood product. This might prove to be a more remunerative outlet than selling or giving away the meat products in the domestic or foreign markets. While some consumers and others might look with disfavor on the idea of any human food products being converted into animal feed, the fact that such a diversion program might improve the quality of the product has to be considered. The poorer quality food could be included in the products diverted from the consumer market.

Marketing orders and agreements seem to operate best with a strong producer group (or groups) representing producers at the hearings where orders are drawn up and amended. The production of livestock is widely scattered geographically. Producers and their organizations have different interests and objectives. There are many different kinds and types of organizations that represent livestock producers. These conditions would make it extremely difficult for livestock producers and their organizations to agree on proper provisions for a marketing order. Perhaps in a more limited geographical area, such as the Corn Belt, marketing orders might stand a better chance of being successful than marketing orders drawn up on a national basis. If such success results in higher livestock prices, however, livestock production in other areas of the country might be increased and thus nullify the price gains made under the regional order.

It is clear that the application of the marketing agreement and order concept to livestock products would not be easy. There would be many administrative difficulties in any workable plan. Their nature would, of course, depend upon the purpose or objective of the marketing order. Collecting money for advertising and promotion, for example, would be an easier job for a marketing order than the task of raising and keeping livestock prices above what they would have been if the order had not been instituted. The use of marketing orders is an attempt by producers and others to add stability to the marketing of a particular product at minimum expense to the government. The difficulties likely to be encountered in any workable system of marketing orders for livestock raise two as yet unanswered questions. Can a workable, equitable, and acceptable marketing order be developed for livestock? Are there alternative methods of achieving stability—public or private—that would be preferable to marketing orders?

The Future

Between now and 1975 a variety of forces will be working toward greater stability in the livestock and meat industry. In general, research and education will provide producers with more reliable price forecasts. Production research will give producers more control over the elements responsible for variations in production. The growth of production under contract will be a further stabilizing force. The larger, more efficient marketing organizations of the future will be in a position to take a more positive approach to regulating market supplies. The government too will be operating programs designed, in part at least, to add stability to the industry. The net result will be some reduction in both the cyclical and the seasonal variations in production and prices for both hogs and cattle.

Individual firms within the meat economy will achieve much greater stability than the meat economy as a whole, particularly with respect to the supply of livestock. A system of contracts or other forms of vertical integration can help assure particular firms of a more stable supply of products of the desired kind and quality.

Various degrees of stability will be attained at the different functional levels of the meat economy. Apparently, a system of contracts or informal arrangements between retailers and wholesalers and meat packers and processors would make these levels of the meat economy more stable. Meat packers and processors would be protected in that they have contracted for livestock supplies. If they contracted for supplies at a higher than market price, however, or contracted for too large a quantity of supplies, there would be a chance for loss. The position of marketing agencies would be similar to that of meat packers and processors. Stability might be increased, but the possibility of loss and need for adjusting quantities would always be present. Under a contract system of production, producers would be able to adjust the quantities put under contract. Changes in price paid for livestock would be in response to projected supply and demand conditions in the market. While the instability of livestock production and prices is likely to be reduced between 1959 and 1975, instability will continue to be an industry problem throughout the period.

Chapter IX

SUMMARY

THE BULK of the foregoing study has been devoted to a description of the present state of the meat economy, the direction of development of various components of that economy, and projections for its future. Our central theme has been the multiplicity and ever-presence of change—past, present, and future—in the organization of the industry, in its technology, and in the demands of the consumer.

Since it is the consumer who ultimately determines what will be purchased and where, his changing demands are crucial in setting the direction the industry will take. With his increasing patronage of the chain store, he has upset the past relation of the meat retailer to the rest of the meat economy and given him more bargaining power than he has ever had before. This change has occurred in part because individual retailers and groups of retailers now purchase and sell far larger volumes of meat products. It is also because some retail groups have begun fulfilling, or have been threatening to fulfill, the functions of other segments of the economy.

In part, of course, the technological development of the meat industry is a reflection of the technological revolution affecting agriculture as a whole. And in part it has been the result of competition within the industry. But here, too, consumer demand has played an important role, for the public has made clear that it wants particular kinds of meat with particular built-in services. It is therefore to the present and future demands of the consumer that we shall turn first.

Forces Affecting the Meat Economy from Without

Changes in Consumer Demand

The projections for population, income, and meat consumption indicate that by 1975 total meat consumption will be between 50% and 60% greater than in 1956. Most of the increased consumption will result from population increases, for only a modest increase in per capita consumption is expected. Consumers will continue to favor beef over pork, but the relative decrease in pork prices compared with prices of beef will help sustain pork consumption. The expected increase in total meat consumption means that firms at all levels of the meat economy must expand in order to handle much larger quantities of meat. Production of livestock and meat is expected to increase as fast as or faster than the anticipated demand. There will therefore be downward pressure on livestock prices during much of the period between 1959 and 1975 so that there will be a "buyers'" market.

A higher percentage of the meat in the future will be consumed away from home, at hotels, restaurants, and institutions and the H.R.I. buyers will continue to seek more services from their suppliers (e.g., portion-controlled cuts). There will also be a relative increase between 1959 and 1975 in the demand for processed meat items as compared with the demand for fresh meat. Meat products, fresh and processed, containing more built-in maid services for the housewife will also be in a strong demand position during the 1959–1975 period.

Consumer demand for meat, as measured by consumer expenditures, will be more elastic than the general consumer demand for food. Firms in the meat economy should therefore pay close attention to the kind and type of service added to meat products. Research on new or changed products and packages combined with market testing of the products would show how consumer expenditures for meat products could be raised.

Changes in Technology

Agriculture in general and the livestock and meat industry in particular are in the midst of a technological revolution. The shift from animal power to machine power, the improvement in crop varieties and breeding stock, the increased use of fertilizer and lime, the availability of equipment and machinery, improved feeds, and better management are only a few of the more spectacular changes that have occurred or are occurring in agricultural production. There have also been many technological changes in marketing agricultural products. Transportation and refrigeration have been improved. New marketing facilities have been built and changes have been made in established facilities. Meat packers and processors have adopted new processes and packages. Modern slaughtering and processing facilities have recently been put in operation and older plants have been modernized. Certainly food retailing has changed with the advent of the supermarket and self-service merchandising. Technological changes as well as others, in the home have influenced the kind, quality, and form of products demanded by consumers.

There is no way of knowing the rate of technological development in the future or the rate at which new developments will be adopted. The vigor of the search for new and better products and methods of operation apparent at all levels of the meat economy makes it very likely that the rate of technological development in the future will be as fast as in the past, if not faster. Many current technological developments will increase in importance by 1975, and new ones will appear, for example, quick frozen cuts and packages of meat for consumers will become more important; improved ways of identifying meat quality both in the live animal and in meat products will be developed; some meats, particularly lower quality products, will be tenderized commercially; processes will be perfected that increase shelf life of meat products such as treatment with antibiotics or radiation and new packages or processes will be developed that allow the meat cutting and processing now done in the retail store to be satisfactorily shifted to the grocery warehouse or meat packing and processing plant.

Factors Affecting the Meat Economy from Within

Competition

As in other sectors of the American economy, the major motivation of firms in the meat industry is an increase in sales volume, profit, and return on investment. The ensuing competition results in a continuous search for new and different products and for increased efficiency. In some segments of the industry, economies of scale will result in the development of fewer but larger firms. In other segments apparent diseconomies will lead to the development of smaller plants and firms.

Firms not providing needed services or providing inadequate services will find it difficult to survive unless they have strong enough market influence to prevent the entry of new firms.

Changes in Retail Market Power

Spectacular and significant changes have occurred in the retail sector of the meat economy. The share of the market handled by chain stores has continued to increase although at a decreasing rate. There has been a substantial growth in the proportion of sales by voluntary and cooperative groups. These group movements are designed to give independent stores the same advantages and economies in buying that chain stores enjoy. The share of the food business done by unaffiliated independent stores has declined appreciably in recent years but shows signs of leveling off in the late 1960's. The bulk of food store sales for both independents and chains is through supermarkets. Chains have been more successful than voluntary or cooperative groups in closing small stores and thus increasing the percentage of business done through supermarkets. Independents, however, are as rapidly as possible following suit in closing small stores and opening larger ones. In addition to new stores being built, a considerable number of older stores have been remodeled each year. There has been a movement in some areas toward an increase in superettes or smaller bantam-sized markets. In some areas large discount-type houses handling food and nonfood items have appeared. As of 1959, chain companies handled about 22% of all meat consumed.[1] This percentage is expected to increase by 1975. Perhaps the most significant development to come will be the increased purchases of meat by voluntary and cooperative groups and grocery wholesalers. This means that by 1975 practically all meat will be purchased by some kind of group buyer. The buyers will be fewer in number and on the average buying larger quantities of meat. Such a situation puts increased bargaining power into the hands of the retail buyer.

Individual retail accounts are large and the loss of an account can create at least temporary difficulties for a supplier. The expected heavy livestock supplies in relation to demand also will create further problems for the already harried supplier. Competition will be keen, especially for the business of the large accounts. Such a market situation makes shopping around for "special deals" or price concessions from suppliers very inviting to the retailer. In general, however, there seems to be an honest feeling on the part of retail buyers that good suppliers ought to be protected. This does not mean that inefficiencies in meat packing and processing or lack of service will be tolerated for long. What it does mean is that suppliers on the average can expect to be held to the margin that is high enough to keep those considered to be good suppliers in business. At the same time the margin will be low enough so that the retail companies will not be able to afford to go into meat

[1] This figure includes meat consumed outside the home as well as in the home.

packing and processing operations themselves. Thus, the retail buyers are in a position where they can influence various factors, including price, important in the transfer of product ownership from meat packers and processors or wholesalers to retail outlets.

While some stores and some groups are centralizing meat buying, other organizations, particularly the larger chains, are tending to decentralize their operations. It appears that on balance there will be increased centralization of buying functions, and buying will still be controlled by the main headquarters of the larger chains and voluntary or cooperative groups.

Retail stores will find it advisable to begin to move processing operations out of the store to central warehouse facilities or back to the packing plant. The speed with which the development can be pushed will depend upon the availability and rate of adoption of appropriate technology. In general, the retail buyers are going to be seeking more uniform products. Such buyers will also be interested in what they consider to be higher quality products. Retail buyers will in general expect more services to be performed on the meat products. Food retailers will be interested in carrying more processed and packaged items with consumer appeal. Many food retailers will be interested in products packed under their own store or house label. Retailers will increasingly try to differentiate their meat in some way from meat carried by other stores. These changes in retail buying mean that (1) specifications on the meat bought by retailers will become increasingly rigid and will be more strongly enforced, (2) more and more of the meat purchased will be bought on some kind of specification basis over and above U. S. or Packer Grade, and (3) individual buyers will be seeking larger quantities of meat each week that meet their particular specifications.

The net result of the actual and prospective changes at the retail level has been a shifting in the balance of power in the meat industry. The power pendulum, once centered over the packing and processing industry, has shifted to the retail buyer. These buyers are in a position to demand and get what they want in the way of product, delivery, packing, and in some cases, price. The buying and selling of meat products for retail stores appears to be very competitive even though both the buyer and seller in many cases represent relatively large organizations. Retail buyers in general are seeking a particular quality and cut at the lowest possible price. Meat packers and processors are trying to sell their product at the highest possible price. Both buyers and sellers have several alternatives open to them.

The Specialization of Meat Wholesaling

In the wholesale sector, the major changes have been a decline in the importance of the branch house operations of national packers, a large increase in the quantities of meat products shipped directly to retail stores, and an increase in the importance of independent meat wholesalers. Packer branch houses have declined for two reasons. Improvements in refrigeration and transportation made a large number of once needed branch houses obsolete. Newer, more efficient branch house units have been handling the combined volume of a number of the older units. At the same time, however, the changes in retail market structure made it expedient for the large packers to service retailers and others directly from their packing or processing plants. Since many retail buyers had their own warehouse facilities, branch houses were not needed merely for storage. Many voluntary and cooperative groups and other grocery wholesalers have instituted meat buying and merchandising plans for their retailers. In most cases these wholesale organizations buy the meat from packers or processors with delivery scheduled directly to the store or store warehouse. In a few cases the wholesaler also maintains warehouse facilities or otherwise handles the product.

There has been a striking increase in the number of independent meat wholesalers who buy from packers and processors. These wholesalers provide a variety of services but their chief customers are the H.R.I. trade. This segment of the market has grown rapidly both in amount of product moving through these channels and in terms of services provided. Individual portion-control cuts ready for cooking are prepared for many of the customers in the H.R.I. market. Retail stores and others also secure a portion of their needs for extra wholesale cuts or specialty products from these independent wholesalers.

The wholesaling segment of the industry will become very competitive as meat packers and processors assume additional wholesaling functions. The H.R.I. market will expand. Nevertheless, smaller, less well-financed specialized meat wholesaling firms are going to be under increased pressure to sustain their income level. Such firms may merge with larger organizations or gradually go out of business. A well-organized wholesale business of sufficient volume for efficient operation should be able to compete successfully with large national packers for the wholesale meat business in any area. Such a wholesaler can supply personalized services difficult for a large national organization to provide. The specialized meat wholesalers will continue to grow in importance as meat suppliers for the H.R.I. trade during the early 1960's, but there will be a resurgence of meat packers and processors into the H.R.I. market in the late 1960's or early 1970's. The resurgence will come about as meat packers and processors perform more and more of the specialized wholesaling functions at their geographically decentralized plants. Meat packers and processors will also merge, buy, or otherwise acquire control over specialized meat wholesaling operations.

Increased Competition in Meat Packing

Meat packers and processors are going to be faced with a market consisting for the most part of a few buyers buying meat in relatively large quantities and with definite specifications. The packers may be able to negotiate informal or formal arrangements with retail buyers covering specified minimum quantities of product to be taken at some future time. Retail buyers will put pressure on packers for additional uniformity in quality, quantity, and price. Except for those products where freshness is a significant factor, it seems likely that most of the processing of meat products will be done by specialized meat packers and processors. In response to the demands of retail buyers more of these products will be prepared on a custom basis and packed under the retailer's brand or label. Currently much of the cutting, packaging, and some processing such as the making of hamburger is done in the retail store. As soon as appropriate technology is developed, many of these functions will be centralized. It is also conceivable that some stores may prefer to have the cutting, packaging, and other functions performed for them by meat packers and processors or specialized wholesalers. Technology that will permit the satisfactory performance of these functions outside the retail store has not as yet been developed.

Meat packers and processors faced with this situation should consider a system of contracts as a means of obtaining needed supplies of livestock. Such contracts could be made with individual producers or with marketing agencies controlling supplies of livestock. The numbers of livestock needed would tend to favor contracting with marketing organizations, if such organizations can guarantee fulfillment of the provisions of the contract. While there might be some sort of minimum price written into the contract, the basic pricing mechanism could be tied to the wholesale meat price with appropriate adjustments for processing and handling costs. Contracts would put the meat packers and processors in a position to better equate the supply of livestock with the demand for meat. Contracts with a livestock marketing organization should also enable the meat packer or processor to cut down on livestock procurement costs.

There has been a relatively high degree of concentration in the meat packing and processing industry for many years. There are indications, however, that this concentration as measured by the percentage of the total kill handled by the larger organizations has been declining especially in cattle slaughter. The proportion of hog slaughter accounted for by the relatively large hog slaughterers stayed about the same or increased slightly during the 1948–1954 period. As cattle slaughter increased, a larger percentage was handled by independent slaughterers. The operators of these independent plants were aided by the widespread acceptance of federal grades for beef. The use of such grading standards has made it possible for the smaller plants to sell their products with a minimum of selling and advertising expense.

The large national packers have been engaged in an effort to improve efficiency, lower costs, and increase returns. Old plants have been closed, new plants have been built. In general, there has been a decentralization of the industry taking place with Chicago becoming less important as a meat packing and processing center. Smaller, more specialized plants have been put in operation. Most of these plants are located fairly close to livestock suppliers because of the freight advantage of meat over live animals. While some meat packers fed livestock, such feeding operations remained a relatively insignificant fraction of the total number of livestock fed. Most feeding operations of meat packers were designed to assure the supply of animals of a needed quality throughout the year.

Physical changes made by the larger packing organizations have improved their efficiency, thus increasing the competitive pressure on the inefficient, high-cost firms. Many smaller operations will find it more difficult to compete as they grow from family businesses into large organizations. Smaller, growing firms would do well to explore the possibilities of some kind of combination or merger to spread the additional overhead and speed up growth.

The reduction in importance of packer brands on fresh meat, especially beef, has reduced the advantage that large national packers might have had by merchandising a differentiated product. Large national packers will have to modernize not only their physical facilities but also their sales organizations and policies to meet the competition of the independent plants. The beef packers have become for the most part strictly slaughterers of cattle. Some meat packers will prefer not to be in this position. Some meat packers and processors, possibly some of the larger ones, will tend to concentrate on the production of processed meats and the performance of the wholesaling activity, where the packer brands can be utilized to advantage in merchandising the product.

Producer groups and others will be increasingly interested in having livestock slaughtered on a custom basis. Custom slaughtering and processing may provide an added volume of business for the meat packer or processor and, depending upon the margin obtained, could be a profitable operation.

Changes in Livestock Buying and Marketing Organizations

There has been a long-term down trend in the use of terminal markets as an outlet for livestock. This trend has been more noticeable for hogs than for cattle or sheep. The proportion of hogs sold direct to packers or processors increased almost continuously since World War I. Local auction markets have increased in relative importance in all areas of the country during the 1930–1959 period.

Many livestock markets do a relatively low volume of business. Facilities are idle or unused during several days of the week. Often these facilities are poorly located or designed. This means that the local assembly and marketing of livestock is a relatively high cost operation needing improvement.

There will be intense competition among livestock markets between 1959 and 1975. The continued growth of direct marketing, either direct to packers or to a marketing organization, will mean that relatively fewer livestock will be marketed at auction or on the terminal market. Many of the livestock markets are too small in volume to be economic units. The relatively lower returns for livestock marketed through such agencies will encourage producers to seek other outlets for their livestock. In part these disadvantages can be overcome by serving a larger territory and operating the marketing facilities more than one day per week. As the markets grow bigger and cover more territory, however, a new difficulty arises. Additional transportation and collection costs are incurred and it is more difficult for distant producers to see their livestock sold. Thus the main advantages of auction selling may be abrogated.

The needed bargaining power and market service demanded by buyers and sellers alike will be a factor favoring the development and growth of fewer, but larger, markets. The potential advantages of producer cooperative marketing organizations seems to be high. A question still remains as to whether the management and the potential members of such organizations will recognize the advantages and be willing to provide the organization with capable managers, some control over livestock production, the needed capital, and adequate volumes of livestock so that it can do an effective job of marketing.

Livestock marketing organizations should be interested in signing contracts with livestock producers in the future. Such contracts would be a necessity if the organization contracts with meat packers and processors or others for the sale of livestock. Even if such selling contracts do not develop as expected, the marketing organizations would find it advantageous to have a contract with its members or patrons. To be effective, the marketing organizations would need to have some degree of control over the kind, quality, and timing of the livestock produced. While a formal contract is not essential in having such control over production, it would help immeasurably. In return, the marketing organization would provide assistance to the producer in the form of credit and management help, and above all assure the producer of a good market for his products.

Increases in Contract Livestock Production

Livestock producers will be under increasing competitive pressure between 1959 and 1975. The difference between average costs of production and lower costs achieved by more efficient operations will encourage greater production by what might be considered nonfarm firms. Feed companies and others will feed more cattle and hogs in large-scale commercial feedlots. Commercial cattle feedlots in the West will expand in number and volume of production. Such feedlots will also become more numerous in the Corn Belt. Commercial hog feedlots will develop and grow in the Corn Belt and probably in the South. As a higher and higher percentage of the fed livestock comes from the lower cost commercial units, livestock prices can be expected to move downward in response to the lower production costs. This will put a further squeeze on the small livestock producers, who will have to increase production and improve efficiency of production if their incomes are to be maintained. Competitive pressure resulting from the development of commercial feedlots will serve to intensify the present trend toward fewer and larger livestock production units. Even though the commercial feedlot expansion will be considerable by 1975, most of the livestock will still be produced at that time by small producers. Livestock production in the South and in the West will increase at a faster rate than in the Corn Belt during the 1959–1975 period. In 1975, however, the Corn Belt will still be the area of greatest concentration of both beef and hog production.

Livestock producers will continue to have several alternatives open to them in the sale of their livestock. Local auction markets and terminal markets will continue to sell livestock. Packer buyers will continue to purchase livestock either at the concentration yards or at the farm on either a cash or contract basis. Local dealers, producer cooperative marketing organizations, and possibly some feed suppliers will also operate concentration yards where livestock can be sold by producers. In some cases the livestock may be sold to the local dealer, cooperative, or other agency, but delivered direct to the meat packer or processor.

Many livestock producers will find it desirable and prudent to enter into a contract covering the production and marketing of their livestock. In addition to services rendered under the contract such as financing and management help, and assistance in getting breeding stock, the organization controlling a relatively large volume of livestock should be in a position to do a better job of marketing for individual producers. They would be able to sort and grade the product for specific markets, and to tap distant markets not ordinarily open to the individual producer. In addition, the marketing organization would be large enough and would have capital enough so that it could move into meat packing and processing and even meat retailing if such moves seemed warranted. In any event, the larger marketing organization with a large volume of livestock should be in a somewhat more advantageous bargaining position with meat packers and processors or food retailers than an individual producer.

Concentration and Integration in the Future

While numerous changes in concentration have taken place, the increased concentration occurring in food retailing is particularly significant. The vertical structure has changed also. Vertical integration seems to bear both a cause and effect relation to concentration. It may enable a particular firm or segment of the industry to increase its relative concentration. At the same time, increased concentration in one segment may lead to vertical integration with other segments of the industry.

Crucial questions about the future are: (1) How far are the

changes in concentration and vertical integration likely to go? (2) What will the limiting factors be? (3) What problems will such developments leave unsolved? (4) What problems will be intensified?

The ultimate upper limits of concentration and vertical integration would be one large firm in complete control of the livestock and meat industry—clearly a monopoly situation. There are many gradations between the industry organization of 1959 and this ultimate extreme. In general, concentration at all levels of the meat economy is expected to increase. Likewise, more and more of the products will be produced through partially or completely integrated systems of production and marketing.

There will be changes in the relative bargaining power of the various components of the industry. The ability of a single firm, group of firms, or segment of the industry arbitrarily to set prices as a monopolist seems remote. The operation of the competitive system and regulatory activities of the government would tend to prevent such a market situation from continuing for any extended periods of time.

The single effective means of controlling a market (arbitrarily setting prices) is by controlling supply. No enterprise in the meat economy appears to be able to do this. Control over supply could only be achieved through the limitation of the entry of new firms into the industry. The relative ease of entry into all levels of the meat economy will continue and thus makes the control over supply impossible. Control could not be achieved short of government intervention. It is very doubtful that any group—retailer, wholesaler, processor, or other—has sufficient control over consumer preferences to affect the market. There is no evidence of such a position among firms in any level of the industry.[1]

Individual firms or groups of firms, however, can control

[1] G. Mehren, Address before the National Institute of Animal Agriculture, Lafayette, Indiana, April 21, 1958.

supply in specified regions or even for the country as a whole for short periods of time. It would take time for new firms to enter the industry, for new integrators to discover the situation, for counterbargaining agencies to develop, or for the government to move in with supervision and regulation.

There are several ways in which the government can act to correct situations in which a firm (or group of firms) appears to be acting as a monopolist. Better communications and market information concerning individual markets would tend to attract buyers and sellers to or from those markets when prices appear out of line. The government could establish regulations over various segments of the meat economy when there is the threat or suggestion that one or a number of firms have an undue share of the market or are acting in a manner contrary to the public interest.

An analysis of the regulatory role of government goes far beyond the scope of this report, but as it does affect the firms within the meat economy it must certainly be considered.

Government as a regulatory agency has been assigned the task of maintaining competition, promoting technological progress, improving efficiency, preserving freedom, and striving toward a host of other goals basic to democracy and economic progress. Many of these goals are conflicting, and in the democratic process compromises between the goals must be made.

The food retailing segment of the meat economy will come under increasingly close scrutiny of government regulatory agencies as concentration and market influence in food retailing continue to increase. Likewise, producer groups and others can expect to come under increasingly close surveillance as they increase their power position in the industry.

Although government regulation will not halt the basic movement toward increased concentration and vertical integration, such action by the government may alter the rate of the change.

Unsolved and Intensified Problem Areas

While the moves toward increased concentration and vertical integration will solve some of the problems of the industry, other problem areas remain unsolved or are intensified.

Instability

The instability of livestock production creates problems throughout the entire meat economy. The longer term cycles in the production of cattle and hogs and the shorter term seasonal variations in livestock numbers within the year bring movements in livestock prices in the opposite direction. The longer run cycles are largely the result of imperfect price forecasts on the part of the producers. The seasonal variations in livestock supply are more closely associated with the bunching of animal births.

Increased use of contracts in the production of livestock would tend to help even out some of the seasonal swings in production. Greater stability would also result with contractual production if the parties in control of the livestock were more successful in predicting future price relations than farmer producers have been. Through vertically integrated arrangements, changes in the final demand for meat would be more rapidly transmitted to the producer. Therefore, contracts or integration would tend to even out short-run fluctuations but may perhaps make the longer run fluctuations even greater. It is likely that future changes in the market structure will not significantly reduce the instability in agricultural production and prices. Other ways will have to be found to solve this problem of the livestock and meat economy.

Research and Education

Changes in market structure will call for continuing increased efforts in research and education. The changes will necessitate the use of better qualified and better trained personnel at all levels of the meat economy. While some of these people will come from the present ranks of the firms, colleges and universities will contribute to the training of management in at least certain segments of the industry.

The competitiveness of the industry in the future will put a premium on further research. Much of this research will be carried on by individual firms or groups of firms through trade organizations. There are, however, problems that go beyond the scope of individual firms or segments and that affect the entire meat economy. These problems will often be neglected unless some government-sponsored research agencies or private research agencies undertake to study them. The proper role of government-sponsored research has not been well understood or agreed upon by the various components of the meat economy. There seems to be little argument over government research and education on problems of producers and producer groups. There is no such general agreement in the meat economy over the role of the U. S. Department of Agriculture and the various land grant colleges regarding problems of meat packers and processors, wholesalers, and retailers. Opportunities for assistance may be present, but the industry groups concerned for the most part remain unconvinced of the opportunities or the propriety of accepting such help.

The vertical integration expected to develop in the meat economy in the future calls for a tremendous amount of research and investigation if it is to move forward on a sound footing. Many of the problems arising from such integration are broad in scope and encompass the entire meat economy. Research on such broad problem areas might best be handled by governmental or private research groups. An expanded system of contracts is expected to develop between or among firms in the meat economy. Considerable research and experimentation will be required to develop contracts that are workable and equitable. A system of production and marketing under contract may call for an entirely new or greatly remodeled pricing mechanism in the livestock and meat industry. Research and investigation should help the meat economy to better appraise the various alternatives that might be used to establish livestock and meat prices at the different functional levels.

The Problem of Adjusting Production

The basic problem of agricultural adjustment—the expansion of supply faster than the expansion of demand—is not likely to be overcome by changes in concentration or vertical integration in agriculture.

Changes in the technology of agriculture, and livestock production, are likely to come faster or at least as fast in the future as in the past. These technological changes will make for an even greater expansion of supply. Concentration and vertical integration in the meat economy may tend toward greater control over supply, but such control will not be extensive enough or great enough to make adjustment possible. Increased concentration and integration may tend to speed up the adoption of new technology and thus possibly further aggravate the adjustment problem of agriculture.

It is apparent that devices and methods other than increased vertical integration and concentration will have to be employed for a successful solution to the production adjustment problem of agriculture. While the changes occurring and likely to occur in the meat economy will solve some problems, they will also create new or intensified problem areas. Such is the never ending dynamic pattern of change.

APPENDIX TABLES

Appendix Table 1. Meat and Meat Animal Imports and Exports, 1950–1957

Imports—Meat Animals

Year	Cattle Dutiable	Cattle Breeding*	Cattle Total	Sheep & Lambs Dutiable	Sheep & Lambs Breeding*	Sheep & Lambs Total	Hogs Dutiable	Hogs Breeding*	Hogs Total	Imports—Meat Carcass wt. equivalent mil. lbs.
1957	702,915	24,938	727,853	17,832	†	17,832	746	†	746	524
1956	140,805	18,554	159,359	3,158	†	3,158	381	†	381	356
1955	296,016	18,361	314,377	7,640	†	7,640	6,590	†	6,590	399
1954	70,680	15,376	86,056	1,480	†	1,480	30,715	†	30,715	412
1953	177,160	21,066	198,226	868	1,283	2,151	24,030	395	24 425	438
1952	138,048	2,413	140,461	304	603	907	185	11	196	506
1951	219,821	19,138	238,959	14,312	2,591	16,903	950	535	1,485	542 ‡
1950	438,285	22,684	460,969	97,127	3,340	100,467	120	865	985	384 ‡

Exports—Meat Animals

Year	Cattle Nonbreeding	Cattle Breeding	Cattle Total	Sheep & Lambs Total	Hogs Total	Exports—Meat § Carcass wt. equivalent mil. lbs.
1957	6,916	37,029	43,945	36,029	3,907	267
1956	12,621	24,239	36,860	60,410	10,255	257
1955	10,396	24,505	34,901	26,113	4,378	195
1954	4,017	17,235	21,252	11,589	887	165
1953	4,087	10,703	14,790	33,888	1,407	194
1952	3,581	7,231	10,812	6,303	1,748	185
1951	1,991	6,404	8,395	1,087	935	157 ‡
1950	2,119	6,232	8,351	2,517	1,444	135 ‡

* Includes other imports not subject to duty. † Included with "animals for breeding, N.E.C."
‡ Does not include West Germany.
§ Includes exports to Puerto Rico and Virgin Islands, exports to Guam included 1952–1957.

Source: U. S. Agricultural Marketing Service, Statistical Bulletin No. 230, *Livestock and Meat Statistics, 1957*, (Washington, Government Printing Office, July 1958), pp. 291–294.

Appendix Table 2.   Total Pounds of Red Meat and Poultry Produced and Consumed, 1950–1959

Year	Beef	Veal	Lamb & Mutton	Pork (excluding Lard)	Total Red Meat	Poultry *	Total Red Meat & Poultry
			Production in Millions of Pounds †				
1959 ‡	14,000	1,200	750	11,750	27,700	6,350	34,050
1958	13,350	1,200	685	10,525	25,760	6,000	31,760
1957	14,211	1,528	707	10,482	26,928	5,458	32,386
1956	14,462	1,632	741	11,218	28,053	5,197	33,250
1955	13,569	1,578	758	10,991	26,896	4,400	31,296
1954	12,963	1,647	734	9,870	25,214	4,613	29,827
1953	12,407	1,546	729	10,006	24,688	4,325	29,013
1952	9,650	1,169	648	11,527	22,994	4,238	27,232
1951	8,837	1,059	521	11,481	21,898	4,136	26,034
1950	9,534	1,230	597	10,714	22,075	3,789	25,864
			Consumption in Millions of Pounds				
1957	14,232	1,484	710	10,355	26,781	5,304	32,085
1956	14,114	1,572	735	11,143	27,564	4,922	32,486
1955	13,306	1,531	753	10,834	26,424	4,284	30,708
1954	12,737	1,591	730	9,549	24,607	4,470	29,077
1953	12,113	1,485	735	9,900	24,233	4,165	28,398
1952	9,548	1,099	640	11,112	22,399	4,098	26,497
1951	8,472	1,003	517	10,857	20,489	3,946	24,435
1950	9,529	1,206	596	10,390	21,721	3,709	25,430

* Chickens including commercial broilers and turkey, ready to cook (eviscerated) basis.

† Production of red meats is carcass weight equivalent of production from total United States slaughter.

‡ Projected forecast.

Source: Production from *Livestock and Meat Situation*, November 1958, p. 6, and March 1959, p. 12. Consumption of red meats from *Livestock and Meat Statistics, 1957*, pp. 283, 284. Consumption of poultry from *Supplement for 1956 to Consumption of Food in the U. S. 1909–1952*, Agriculture Handbook No. 62, September 1957, pp. 70, 71, and *Supplement for 1957 to Consumption of Food in the U. S. 1909–1952*, Agriculture Handbook No. 62, August 1958, p. 16.

Appendix Table 3.   Total United States Population July 1 Each Year, 1950–1958

Year	Population	Year	Population
1958	174,060	1953	159,638
1957	171,196	1952	157,028
1956	168,176	1951	154,360
1955	165,270	1950	151,683
1954	162,417		

Source: U. S. Bureau of the Census, *Current Population Reports*, P-25, No. 191 (Washington, Government Printing Office, December 11, 1958), p. 1.

Appendix Table 4.   Number of Self-Service Meat Departments, 1951–1958

Year	Chain	Independent	Total
1958	10,200	9,800	20,000
1957	9,750	9,200	18,950
1956	8,750	8,600	17,350
1955	7,750	7,250	15,000
1954	6,500	5,000	11,500
1953	5,750	3,750	9,500
1952	4,500	3,300	7,800
1951	3,200	2,100	5,300

Source: "Facts in Grocery Distribution," annual issue of *Progressive Grocer*, 1954, 1956, 1958, and 1959 editions.

Appendix Table 5.   Percentage of Supermarkets with Self-Service Meat Departments, 1951–1957

Year	Complete	Partial	None
1957	87	10	3
1956	86	10	4
1955	82	11	7
1954	62	20	18
1953	53	24	23
1952	49	23	28
1951	41	21	38

Source: *Super Market Industry Speaks* (Chicago, Super Market Institute), 1954, 1956, 1957, 1958 editions.

Appendix Table 6. Household Expenditures for Meat by Household Income, 1956

Annual Household Income	U. S. Households		Percentage of Total Expenditures				Ave. Expenditure per Household			
	Number	% of Total	Fresh *	Frozen †	Canned ‡	Total	Fresh	Frozen	Canned	Total
Under $2,000	8,610	15%	10%	12%	11%	10.2%	$112.00	$1.20	$3.10	$116.30
$2,000–$2,999	7,080	14	12	14	13	12.2	156.00	1.70	4.30	168.00
$3,000–$3,999	7,510	15	15	15	16	15.2	195.00	1.80	5.10	210.90
$4,000–$4,999	9,250	19	20	15	22	20.0	204.00	1.40	5.40	219.80
$5,000–$6,999	9,680	20	23	20	21	23.0	232.00	1.80	4.90	238.70
$7,000–$9,999	4,680	9	13	12	10	13.1	261.00	2.20	5.20	268.40
$10,000 and over	2,330	5	7	12	7	7.3	274.00	4.30	6.80	285.10
Totals	49,140	100%	100% (93%)	100% (5%)	100% (2%)	100%	$194.00	$1.80	$4.80	$200.60

* Fresh meat, meat products, and dishes.
† Frozen meat, meat products, and dishes.
‡ Canned and jarred meat, meat products and dishes.

Source: *Life Study of Consumer Expenditures*, Supplement (New York, Time Incorporated, 1958).

Appendix Table 7. Index of Consumer Prices for Meats, Chicken, and Fish, All Foods Consumed at Home, and Consumer Price Index, 1950–1957
(1947–1949 = 100)

	Meat, Chicken and Fish	All Food	Consumer Price Index
1957	105	114	120
1956	97	110	116
1955	102	110	114
1954	108	112	115
1953	110	112	114
1952	116	115	114
1951	117	113	111
1950	105	101	103

Source: *National Food Situation,* July 1958, p. 55

Appendix Table 8. Distribution of the Population by Age as Percentage of Total Population, 1950–1980

Age	1950	1955	1957	1960	1965	1970	1975	1980
Under 5	10.8	11.3	11.2	11.3	10.8	11.4	11.6	11.8
5–9	8.8	10.4	10.5	10.6	10.8	10.3	10.7	10.9
10–14	7.4	8.2	8.7	9.5	9.8	9.9	9.4	9.8
15–19	7.0	6.6	6.9	7.4	8.8	9.0	9.1	8.6
20–24	7.4	5.8	6.3	6.3	6.9	8.1	8.2	8.3
25–29	8.1	7.1	6.7	6.1	5.8	6.4	7.4	7.5
30–34	7.6	7.6	7.2	6.6	5.6	5.4	5.9	6.8
35–44	14.3	14.0	13.6	13.3	12.4	10.7	9.7	9.8
45–54	11.6	11.6	11.6	11.5	11.3	10.9	10.1	8.7
55–64	8.9	8.9	8.7	8.6	8.8	8.9	8.6	8.3
65–69	3.3	3.3	3.2	3.3	3.3	3.2	3.3	3.4
70 +	4.9	5.4	5.4	5.5	5.8	5.9	6.1	6.2
Total Population * in 1,000's	151,683	165,270	171,196	180,492	196,056	214,251	234,810	258,079

* Total U. S. population including overeases armed forces July 1 each year.

Source: 1950 and 1955, *Current Population Reports,* P-25, No. 63, November 2, 1955, p. 4. Other years from *Current Population Reports,* P-25, No. 187, November 10, 1958, p. 24. Revisions in total population from *Current Population Reports,* P-25, No. 191, December 11, 1958, p. 1.

The Meat Economy

Appendix Table 9. Value of Food * to Civilian Consumers by Channel, 1929–1957

Year	Retail Value of Home Produced Food	Retail Value of Food Furnished & Sold by Eating Places †	Retail Value Through Other Channels ‡	Total Retail Value of All Food (100%) (Billions)
1957	7.5%	16.7%	75.8%	$63.6
1956	8.0	16.6	75.4	61.3
1955	8.2	16.4	75.4	58.6
1954	8.5	16.0	75.5	57.6
1953	9.4	15.8	74.8	57.6
1952	9.8	15.3	74.9	57.4
1951	9.9	15.3	74.8	55.6
1950	11.9	15.3	74.8	50.4
1949	11.2	15.7	73.2	49.2
1948	12.2	15.6	72.2	50.8
1947	12.8	15.3	71.8	47.6
1946	14.7	16.5	68.8	40.1
1945	17.2	17.5	65.2	32.5
1944	17.1	16.1	66.8	30.4
1943	17.7	15.1	67.2	29.9
1942	15.6	13.7	70.6	26.2
1941	15.6	13.8	70.5	22.4
1940	16.4	13.8	69.7	19.5
1939	17.5	14.3	68.2	18.9
1938	17.5	13.2	69.3	18.9
1937	17.8	11.4	70.8	20.2
1936	17.7	8.9	73.4	20.3
1935	18.7	8.6	72.7	18.7
1934	18.1	9.6	72.3	17.7
1933	19.7	11.5	68.8	15.7
1932	19.9	14.1	66.0	15.6
1931	19.3	14.6	66.1	19.2
1930	18.5	12.9	68.6	23.3
1929	18.0	12.7	69.3	24.5

* Excluding alcoholic beverages.

† Includes restaurants, boarding houses, institutions, hospitals, and the like, including off-premise sale of candy and other foods.

‡ Includes retail stores, direct by manufacturers and hucksters and other similar outlets.

Source: Unpublished data by Marguerite Burk, Head, Consumption Section, Statistical and Historical Research Branch, United States Department of Agriculture.

**Appendix Table 10.   Central Warehousing and Group Affiliation
by Size of Supermarket Companies, 1957**

Sales Group (in millions)	Own Central Warehouse	Belong to Cooperative	Belong to Voluntary	No Central Warehouse or Affiliation
	Percentage of Companies *			
Up to $2	1%	38%	28%	33%
$2 to $10	20	41	19	24
$10 to $25	70	23	2	14
$25 to $50	100	—	—	—
Over $50	100	9	—	—
All Companies	29%	34%	18%	23%
Total Stores	85%	12%	4%	5%

* The figures do not add up to 100% since some companies used more
than one method.

Source: *Super Market Industry Speaks,* 1958 edition, p. 16.

**Appendix Table 11.   Percentage of Multi-Unit Retailers Buying
from Wholesalers by Number of Retail Stores, 1956–1958**

Year	2–3	4–5	6–10	10–25	25 & over	Total
	Number of Stores in Company					
1958	79%	71%	47%	38%	6%	29%
1957	79%	69	37	36	6	29
1956	——65%——		70	33	5	35

Source: "Facts in Grocery Distribution," 1957, 1958, 1959 editions.

The Meat Economy

Appendix Table 12. Sales, Adjusted for Price Changes, and Percentage Changes in Sales 1939–1948, 1948–1954, and 1939–1954, Packinghouse Branches and Independent Wholesale Distributors and Combined Total by Regions

Type of Distributor and Region	Sales Adjusted for Prices *			
	1954 (in thousands)	Percentage Change		
		1939–48	1948–54	1939–54
Packer Branch Houses				
Northeast	$1,098,209	−29.9	+14.8	−19.6
North Central	500,989	−23.0	+9.2	−15.9
South	874,527	−4.4	+25.1	+19.6
West	223,758	+12.2	+22.1	+37.0
United States	$2,697,483	−19.5	+17.4	−5.5
Independent Meat Wholesalers †				
Northeast	$1,359,289	+23.9	+54.0	+90.8
North Central	690,356	+6.3	+82.4	+93.9
South	425,127	+33.0	+119.1	+191.3
West	391,421	+24.2	+92.5	+139.1
United States	$2,866,193	+20.3	+72.8	+108.0
Total Branch Houses and Meat Wholesalers				
Northeast	$2,457,498	−11.5	+33.6	+18.3
North Central	1,191,345	−12.0	+42.3	+25.2
South	1,299,654	+1.8	+45.5	+48.1
West	615,179	+18.2	+59.1	+88.1
United States	$5,563,676	−6.6	+40.6	+31.4

* All sales adjusted prior to calculation of percentages by the Index of Wholesale Meat Price to reflect 1954 levels of price.
† Grocery wholesalers handling meat are excluded.

Source: Williams, "Economic Effects," p. 28.

Appendix Table 13. Concentration in Livestock Slaughter as a Percentage of Total U. S. Slaughter by Species by the Four Largest * and Ten Largest † Meat Packing Companies, 1947–1956

	Cattle		Calves		Sheep & Lambs		Hogs	
	4 Largest	10 Largest	4 Largest	10 Largest	4 Largest	10 Largest	4 Largest	10 Largest
1956	29.7%	N/A	35.0%	N/A	59.3%	N/A	38.8%	N/A
1955	30.7	37.7%	34.2	40.4%	60.5	68.3%	39.0	57.5%
1954	32.9	39.5	38.2	45.2	61.1	70.8	38.9	58.1
1953	32.9	39.4	37.8	41.2	62.3	72.1	40.6	60.7
1952	33.4	39.4	34.7	38.4	62.3	71.9	40.4	55.5
1951	32.9	37.9	35.9	40.4	63.8	72.5	39.3	53.9
1950	35.9	42.7	36.0	41.3	65.4	75.4	40.2	54.9
1949	37.5	44.3	36.9	42.6	66.7	76.5	39.5	55.7
1948	34.9	40.6	36.7	42.4	64.5	72.5	38.9	53.7
1947	38.2	43.5	39.6	45.0	67.7	77.1	40.4	54.3

* The four largest companies are the four largest slaughterers of each specie each year, except in 1956 when in each specie the four firms used were Swift, Armour, Wilson, and Cudahy.

† The same ten largest for all species for all years: Swift, Armour, Wilson, Hormel, Morrell, Rath, Hygrade, Cudahy, Oscar Meyer, and Dubuque.

Source: 1956—U. S. v. Swift and Company, "Affidavits of Swift Defendants in Opposition to Motion of United States for Summary Judgment," in the United States District Court for the Northern District of Illinois, Eastern Division, May, 1958, p. 1027. All other years calculated from data presented in "Unfair Trade Practices in the Meat Industry," Hearings before the Subcommittee on Antitrust and Monopoly of the Committee on the Judiciary, United States Senate, 85th Congress, 1st Session, May 1–3, 7–10, 15, and 22, 1957, pp. 261–265.

Appendix Table 14. Percentage Distribution of Packers by Types Within Regions and Among Regions, 1955, and Percentage Change by Number of Packers by Type and Region, 1950–1955

| | Types of Meat Packers | | | |
	Federally Inspected	Large Noninspected *	Small Noninspected †	Total
Percentage of Packers by Type Within Region				
Northeast	13.3%	24.5%	62.2%	100.0%
North Central	17.1	30.7	52.2	100.0
South	7.5	31.3	61.2	100.0
West	22.9	30.8	46.3	100.0
United States	14.1%	29.6%	56.3%	100.0%
Percentage Distribution of Meat Packers Among Regions				
Northeast	20.0%	17.7%	23.6%	21.3%
North Central	40.0	34.3	30.7	33.1
South	16.5	32.9	33.8	31.1
West	23.5	15.1	11.9	14.5
United States	100.0%	100.0%	100.0%	100.0%
Percentage Change in Numbers, 1950–1955				
Northeast	0%	+46.1%	−32.5%	−18.2%
North Central	0	+23.9	−16.8	−4.4
South	+15.4	+44.2	+14.8	+22.7
West	+3.4	+11.6	−9.6	−0.8
United States	+3.2%	+31.3%	−12.6%	−0.6%

* Called "other wholesale" in U. S. Department of Agriculture reports.
† Called "local" in U. S. Department of Agriculture reports.

Source: Williams, "Economic Effects," p. 17.

Appendix Table 15. Number of Packing Firms Feeding Livestock 30 Days or More, 1954–1957 *
(Excluding Feeding by Chain Stores)

	Ten Largest Packers			Other Packers			Totals	
	No. of Firms	Head	% of Total Head Fed by Packers	No. of Firms	Head	% of Total Head Fed by Packers	No. of Firms	Head
Cattle								
1957	8	157,144	30.3%	135	361,598	69.7%	143	518,742
1956	6	159,381	35.1	143	294,503	64.9	149	453,884
1955	7	142,853	30.0	146	333,634	70.0	153	476,487
1954	7	156,478	32.2	150	329,648	67.8	157	486,126
Calves								
1957	2	1,948	14.6%	25	11,419	85.4%	27	13,367
1956	2	4,591	31.8	31	9,851	68.2	33	14,442
1955	1	193	2.2	22	8,658	97.8	23	8,851
1954	1	373	4.1	23	8,634	95.9	24	9,007
Hogs								
1957	—	—	—	20	8,431	100%	20	8,431
1956	—	—	—	31	11,921	100	31	11,921
1955	—	—	—	25	8,629	100	25	8,629
1954	—	—	—	25	12,230	100	25	12,230
Sheep								
1957	7	648,362	97.1%	12	19,023	2.9%	19	667,385
1956	5	661,242	91.4	11	12,459	8.6	16	723,701
1955	7	520,364	97.6	19	12,783	2.4	26	533,147
1954	6	1,201,109	97.1	13	36,486	2.9	19	1,237,595

* Total packers engaged in feeding operations 1957—163, 1956—166,
1955—167, 1954—159.

Source: U. S. Agricultural Marketing Service, Packers and Stockyards
Docket #16, " Feeding Operations of Meat Packers" (Washington, Government Printing Office, September 1958), pp.
6 and 7.

Appendix Table 16. Percentage of Cattle and Calves Sold by Farmers Through Various Types of Outlets by State, 1940 and 1956 (Excluding Deacons and Vealers)

State	Terminal 1940†	Terminal 1956	Auction 1940	Auction 1956	Dealer 1940	Dealer 1956	Local Markets 1940	Local Markets 1956	Packer 1940	Packer 1956	Local Retailer* 1956	Other 1940	Other 1956
Illinois	77.6%	78.6%	1.9%	4.0%	3.8%	2.4%	7.2%	2.5%	5.6%	10.9%	.1%	3.9%	1.5%
Indiana	68.5	69.3	4.2	14.9	6.4	.3	8.4	6.4	6.1	8.8	—	6.4	.3
Kentucky	29.5	36.0	25.7	40.6	23.9	6.7	11.5	11.6	8.4	1.9	—	1.0	3.2
Michigan	35.0	33.9	12.0	51.6	24.9	2.1	5.1	2.0	16.0	6.8	2.3	7.0	1.3
Ohio	15.0	23.6	22.2	47.1	18.9	8.8	15.8	2.8	18.8	13.5	3.5	9.3	.7
Wisconsin	37.7	34.9	—	—	24.8	19.6	.1	6.6	23.0	22.2	1.1	14.4	15.6
E. North Central		55.3%		20.5%		5.2%		4.4%		10.9%	.9%		2.8%
Iowa	61.4%	57.4%	3.6%	12.2%	9.9%	4.2%	1.6%	—	20.8%	25.0%	.5%	2.7%	.7%
Kansas	79.9	77.0	7.0	20.5	3.6	.5	2.7	—	4.8	.6	.6	2.0	.3
Minnesota	54.0	79.3	1.4	4.5	7.8	2.8	9.0	—	19.1	11.8	.5	8.7	1.1
Missouri	76.7	87.3	.9	3.0	5.3	1.9	6.4	.3	6.0	3.2	.5	4.7	3.8
Nebraska	74.1	58.7	12.8	32.3	3.5	.4	.9	.5	3.0	.2	—	5.7	7.9
North Dakota	43.0	53.0	1.3	14.0	17.1	8.8	6.0	.7	21.6	21.9	1.1	11.0	.5
South Dakota	48.2	50.2	12.4	26.4	8.6	4.0	2.4	.5	26.4	18.3	—	2.0	.6
W. North Central		66.9%		15.1%		2.8%		.2%		12.7%	.4%		1.9%
Total North Central‡	61.6%	62.8%	6.2%	17.0%	9.7%	3.6%	4.9%	1.7%	12.5%	12.1%	.6%	5.6%	2.2%

* For 1940, "Local Retailer" included under "Other."   † Includes some packer buying stations.
‡ Includes Oklahoma for 1940 figures.

Source: *Marketing Livestock in the Corn Belt Region*, South Dakota Experiment Station Bulletin 365, November 1943, p. 125, and *Livestock Marketing in the North Central Region*, Part I, Research Bulletin 846, Ohio Agricultural Experiment Station, Wooster, Ohio, December 1959, p. 33.

Appendix Table 17. Percentage of Slaughter Hogs and Pigs Sold by Farmers Through Various Types of Outlets by State, 1940 and 1956

State	Terminal 1940	Terminal 1956	Auction 1940	Auction 1956	Dealer 1940	Dealer 1956	Local Market 1940	Local Market 1956	Packer 1940	Packer 1956	Local Retailer* 1956	Other 1940	Other 1956
Illinois	61.9%	51.0%	.2%	2.5%	2.1%	4.6%	19.3%	10.0%	10.5%	26.8%	.1%	6.0%	5.0%
Indiana	50.4	38.2	.7	2.5	1.4	.2	30.9	46.8	12.4	12.1	.1	4.2	.1
Kentucky	34.2	19.9	38.1	33.1	9.0	—	10.6	19.5	6.9	23.7	—	1.2	3.8
Michigan	24.1	10.5	13.2	58.1	13.9	1.7	15.6	20.4	23.9	7.2	1.4	9.3	.7
Ohio	16.2	18.1	15.6	18.5	19.8	.7	24.0	50.1	15.7	12.2	.2	8.7	.2
Wisconsin	23.4	15.5	—	—	25.1	11.8	.4	4.6	33.0	58.2	.1	18.1	9.8
E. North Central		35.5%		8.8%		3.1%		26.8%		22.5%	.2%		3.1%
Iowa	20.2%	14.4%	1.3%	1.1%	24.4%	25.6%	15.4%	—	32.3%	57.5%	—	6.4%	1.4%
Kansas	30.9	49.2	20.6	22.8	9.5	10.9	8.0	.3	28.8	16.8	—	2.2	—
Minnesota	37.2	57.4	.4	.2	13.0	12.7	14.3	1.5	24.1	27.7	—	11.0	.5
Missouri	62.5	74.9	.6	2.1	4.3	.2	8.6	3.6	21.4	18.3	.1	2.6	.8
Nebraska	54.9	30.7	27.1	40.3	3.6	10.9	6.7	—	6.4	9.5	—	1.3	8.6
North Dakota	37.5	55.1	1.1	7.1	9.0	2.4	10.0	7.3	22.0	25.5	.8	20.4	1.8
South Dakota	29.1	31.1	10.1	21.1	4.8	1.8	4.5	—	48.4	44.6	—	3.1	1.4
W. North Central		34.3%		7.1%		16.1%		.9%		39.8%	—		1.8%
Total North Central †	37.8%	34.8%	5.0%	7.8%	12.9%	10.6%	15.4%	11.8%	22.3%	32.5%	.1%	6.6%	2.4%

* For 1940, "Local Retailer" is included under "Other."   † 1940 totals for the region include Oklahoma.

Source: *Marketing Livestock in the Corn Belt Region*, South Dakota Experiment Station Bulletin 365, November 1943, p. 125, and *Livestock Marketing in the North Central Region*, Part I, Research Bulletin 846, Ohio Agricultural Experiment Station, Wooster, Ohio, December 1959, p. 51.

Appendix Table 18.　Total Livestock Marketings and Marketings at Public Stockyards, 1935–1956
(In Thousands)

Year	Cattle				Calves				Hogs				Sheep & Lambs			
	Chicago	Nine Terminals	Total Public Marketings	Total Marketings*	Chicago	Nine Terminals	Total Public Marketings	Total Marketings*	Chicago	Nine Terminals	Total Public Marketings	Total Marketings*	Chicago	Nine Terminals	Total Public Marketings	Total Marketings*
1956	2,482	13,186	23,538	33,530	132	2,140	5,343	15,807	3,198	18,991	36,310	77,840	562	7,627	15,005	22,629
1955	2,317	12,570	22,507	31,418	125	1,871	5,036	15,453	3,291	18,582	34,204	75,381	643	7,631	15,332	21,522
1954	2,271	12,589	23,195	30,622	113	2,176	5,837	15,514	2,979	15,479	29,043	66,012	474	7,515	15,573	21,658
1953	2,298	12,547	22,374	28,307	122	2,193	5,630	14,431	3,187	15,956	29,638	68,572	835	7,834	15,960	20,884
1952	1,853	10,634	18,942	23,652	112	1,969	4,786	12,246	3,869	20,338	38,017	80,448	887	8,086	15,772	20,306
1951	1,623	9,463	17,016	22,638	106	1,781	4,722	11,328	3,907	20,872	38,722	79,142	523	6,678	13,718	18,701
1950	1,780	10,100	17,917	22,664	115	1,850	5,225	12,028	3,670	18,479	35,325	72,673	654	7,996	15,435	19,126
1949	1,850	10,695	18,828	22,905	164	2,000	5,741	12,627	3,425	17,401	33,118	69,249	623	7,814	15,843	20,257
1948	1,694	10,048	18,673	23,417	188	2,056	6,277	12,607	3,342	16,000	30,611	61,790	888	10,604	19,814	23,775
1947	2,089	12,486	22,103	26,981	271	2,640	7,459	13,893	3,318	15,848	29,953	63,499	968	11,598	21,679	26,161
1946	1,960	10,489	21,278	26,267	194	2,514	6,818	13,026	3,541	14,745	28,465	64,409	1,487	13,618	26,147	30,846
1945	2,391	12,617	22,172	27,541	230	2,578	7,070	13,222	3,516	12,958	25,342	61,035	1,875	15,563	27,658	32,316
1944	2,340	12,019	20,513	23,627	287	2,733	7,289	14,323	6,018	24,288	44,511	86,289	2,056	16,864	29,208	32,711
1943	2,143	11,181	18,190	21,310	217	2,007	5,694	11,177	5,792	22,483	41,077	83,187	2,390	17,476	30,467	35,323
1942	2,182	10,702	17,979	20,740	248	2,275	6,681	11,787	5,338	18,431	34,415	67,423	2,596	15,880	28,211	34,662
1941	2,035	9,025	15,228	18,948	244	2,070	6,128	11,001	4,634	15,713	30,659	57,695	2,179	12,359	22,817	30,741
1940	1,926	8,343	14,077	18,413	271	2,182	6,282	10,365	5,385	18,248	34,556	64,262	2,103	12,596	22,754	30,230
1939				18,380				10,076	4,264	13,966	27,974	52,906	2,499	13,118	23,817	29,874
1938				18,552				9,560	4,188	12,488	24,801	46,089	2,564	14,149	25,598	30,332
1937				18,854				10,298	3,968	11,374	22,666	40,665	2,501	13,800	24,979	28,824
1936				19,991				10,029	4,364	14,437	26,399	44,809	2,595	13,210	24,652	28,833
1935				19,041				9,363	3,600	10,444	19,562	32,749	2,941	13,723	25,567	28,356

* Excludes interfarm marketings.　Source: Agricultural Statistics, 1957, pp. 379, 383, 394, 396, 410, 412.

Appendix Table 19. Percentage of Total Feed Consumed by Cattle, Sheep, and Hogs, Derived from Different Sources, Averages 1909–1955

Period	Corn	Other Grain	Commercial By-Products	Seeds and Skim Milk	Hay	Silage and Beet Pulp	Stover and Straw	Pasture
				Beef Cattle				
1909–19	4.1%	1.2%	1.3%	.5%	5.8%	0.6%	10.8%	75.7%
1920–29	5.5	1.6	2.0	.6	6.9	1.2	9.4	72.8
1930–39	7.8	1.6	2.7	.9	7.5	1.6	11.4	66.5
1940–49	9.0	1.7	3.5	.5	11.0	1.5	6.6	66.2
1950–55	10.5	1.4	4.8	.2	14.6	2.1	4.6	61.8
				Sheep				
1909–19	1.9%	2.2%	.9%	—	8.2%	.3%	3.5%	83.0%
1920–29	1.4	3.0	1.1	—	9.8	.8	2.8	81.1
1930–39	2.8	1.7	1.3	—	9.0	1.0	3.4	80.8
1940–49	3.5	1.2	1.4	—	11.5	.9	2.4	79.1
1950–55	3.9	1.5	1.9	—	12.1	.9	2.2	77.5
				Hogs				
1909–19	71.1%	9.6%	10.3%	5.6%	—	—	—	3.4%
1920–29	71.1	11.8	7.6	5.8	—	—	—	3.7
1930–39	67.8	14.0	6.8	7.5	—	—	—	3.9
1940–49	62.6	18.2	10.1	4.2	—	—	—	4.9
1950–55	63.5	16.0	12.7	3.1	—	—	—	4.7
				Poultry				
1909–19	51.4%	22.3%	13.2%	4.5%	—	—	—	8.6%
1920–29	50.2	22.8	16.3	3.5	—	—	—	7.2
1930–39	42.5	29.1	20.3	3.6	—	—	—	4.5
1940–49	40.8	30.0	24.4	1.8	—	—	—	3.0
1950–55	39.6	27.2	30.5	.5	—	—	—	2.2

Source: U. S. Agricultural Research Service, Production Research Report No. 21, *Consumption of Feed by Livestock, 1909–56*, by R. D. Jennings (Washington, Government Printing Office, November 1958), pp. 14–15.

Appendix Table 20. Annual Output of Manufactured Feed, 1948–1958

Year	Total Tonnage (Million Pounds)		Beef & Sheep	Hogs	Dairy	Poultry					Misc.
	U.S. *	AFMA †				Broiler	Turkey	Other	Total		
1958	40.0	19.5	6.2%	14.2%	17.4%	19.8%	5.0%	33.5%	58.3%		3.9%
1957	36.0	17.8	6.0	11.5	18.5	19.8	5.4	34.8	60.0		4.0
1956	35.7	17.6	6.1	9.5	18.6	19.3	5.7	36.8	62.0		3.8
1955	33.6	16.4	6.4	11.0	18.9	17.1	5.0	37.4	59.5		4.2
1954	35.0	17.2	5.3	10.2	18.4	16.9	5.2	39.4	61.5		4.6
1953	33.7	16.3	5.0	8.4	21.0	17.1	4.9	39.0	61.0		4.6
1952	34.4	16.4	7.2	8.6	20.5	15.8	5.6	37.6	59.0		4.7
1951	32.8	15.5	5.0	9.0	19.0	n	n	n	61.0		6.0
1950	29.1	13.5	3.6	8.0	21.0	n	n	n	62.0		5.4
1949	28.5	13.0	2.9	7.3	22.0	n	n	n	61.5		6.3
1948	25.5	10.9	3.0	8.2	25.6	n	n	n	59.0		4.2

* Estimated by the American Feed Manufactures Association.
† American Feed Manufacturers Association.
n Not Available.

Source: Market Research Department, American Feed Manufacturers Association, Chicago, 1959.

Appendix Table 21. Value of Livestock and Livestock Products Marketed by Cooperatives, 1950–1951 to 1955–1956

Period	Gross Value (billions)	Net Value after Adjusting for Duplication * (billions)
1955–1956 †	$1.3	$1.2
1954–1955	1.4	1.3
1953–1954	1.4	1.3
1952–1953	1.6	1.5
1951–1952	1.8	1.6
1950–1951	1.4	1.3

* Does not include the value of sales made by regional cooperatives for local associations with the exception of those sales made by terminal marketing associations for local shipping associations whose patrons received sales proceeds directly from the regional cooperative with which the local association was affiliated.

†Preliminary.

Source: U. S. Farmer Cooperative Service, General Report 48, *Statistics for Farm Cooperatives*, by A. Gessner (Washington, Government Printing Office, July 1958), p. 34.

Appendix Table 22. Number of Livestock on Farms January 1 and Annual Livestock Production, 1955–1959

	Cattle and Calves		Hogs		Sheep and Lambs	
Year	No. on Farms Jan. 1	Production (1000 lbs.)	No. on Farms Jan. 1	Production (1000 lbs.)	No. on Farms Jan. 1	Production (1000 lbs.)
1959	96,851		57,201		32,644	
1958	93,350	27,697,506	50,980	19,420,717	31,337	1,619,938
1957	94,502	26,808,031	51,703	18,471,109	30,840	1,522,253
1956	96,804	27,665,380	55,173	18,858,636	31,273	1,565,814
1955	96,592	28,089,500	50,474	20,044,148	31,582	1,616,714

Source: *Livestock and Meat Statistics, 1957*, pp. 35–37. Revisions and 1959 data from Harold Breimyer, U. S. Department of Agriculture.

Appendix Table 23. Cattle and Calves on Feed by Selected Regions, January 1, 1950–1959

| Year | Penn. | North Central States | | | Texas & Okla. | Western States | | United States Total |
| | | E.N. Central | West North Central | | | Cal. | Others | |
			Corn Belt *	Plains †				
1959 ‡	77	1,326	2,066	1,275	228	504	1,013	6,489
1958	78	1,337	1,943	1,087	163	398	861	5,867
1957	90	1,413	1,911	1,051	218	496	888	6,067
1956	82	1,364	1,806	1,046	214	489	879	5,880
1955	84	1,267	1,780	1,142	200	467	846	5,786
1954	86	1,221	1,675	1,107	199	350	726	5,364
1953	90	1,177	1,845	1,300	263	327	752	5,754
1952	90	1,009	1,510	1,041	241	383	687	4,961
1951	90	967	1,485	936	239	248	569	4,534
1950	88	976	1,491	909	216	196	514	4,390

* Minnesota, Iowa, Missouri.
† North Dakota, South Dakota, Nebraska, and Kansas.
‡ Preliminary.

Source: *Livestock and Meat Situation*, March 1958, p. 8; 1958 and 1959 from Harold Breimyer, U. S. Department of Agriculture.

Appendix Table 24. Estimated Percentage of Annual Beef Production That Is Fed, and the Percentage Distribution of the Beef Supply by Class and Grade, 1945–1956

Year	Total Production (mil. lbs.)	Fed Beef		Total Production by Class			Total Production by Grade*					
		Quantity (mil. lbs.)	% of Total Production	Steer	Heifer	Cow†	Prime	Choice	Good	Standard	Commercial & Utility	Canner & Cutter
1956	14,462	6,536	45.2%	56.4%	12.8%	30.8%	4.2%	32.8%	21.1%	15.9%	12.9%	13.1%
1955	13,568	6,068	44.7	54.2	12.7	33.1						
1954	12,963	5,319	41.0	55.3	11.9	32.8						
1953	12,407	5,254	42.3	58.7	9.7	31.6						
1952	9,650	4,870	50.5	59.5	9.4	31.1	6.0	36.2	18.7	14.0	12.7	12.4
1951	8,837	4,332	49.0	56.8	8.9	34.3						
1950	9,534	4,440	46.6	57.3	9.2	33.5						
1949	9,439	4,604	48.8	58.4	9.8	31.8						
1948	9,075	3,382	37.3	49.3	10.2	40.5						
1947	10,432	3,560	34.1	49.2	11.3	39.5	4.3	26.7	19.8	18.0	16.6	14.6
1946	9,378	3,427	36.5	51.6	10.3	38.1						
1945	10,280	3,980	38.7	51.0	9.7	39.3						

* Revised estimates of grade distribution. Grade designations are those in effect, June 1, 1956, and all years refer to these grades.

† Includes bulls and stags, quantities of which are small as compared to cows.

Source: Livestock and Meat Situation, March 1958, p. 22.

Appendix Table 25. Percentage of Cattle Slaughter by Region, 1947–1957

| | North Atlantic | East North Central | North Central States | | South Atlantic | South Central | | West | |
| | | | West North Central | | | | | | |
			Corn Belt *	Plains †		Texas	Other	California	Other
1957	8.3%	22.4%	17.5%	12.8%	6.6%	6.3%	8.1%	9.2%	8.8%
1956	8.0	21.7	17.3	13.7	6.2	7.1	7.4	9.6	9.0
1955	8.2	21.8	17.1	13.9	6.5	6.8	7.6	9.5	8.6
1954	8.5	22.5	17.1	13.6	6.4	6.8	7.6	9.2	8.3
1953	8.0	22.5	18.0	13.9	5.8	7.0	7.2	9.5	8.1
1952	8.9	23.2	18.0	13.4	5.2	6.6	6.5	10.2	8.0
1951	10.6	24.1	16.6	12.5	5.5	6.0	6.8	10.1	7.8
1950	9.6	24.9	18.4	13.9	5.2	5.3	6.7	8.3	7.7
1949	8.9	24.7	18.7	14.5	5.0	5.2	6.9	8.5	7.6
1948	9.5	25.2	16.3	12.9	6.3	6.4	8.4	7.9	7.1
1947	9.3	24.6	17.3	14.2	5.8	6.5	7.6	7.8	6.9

* Minnesota, Iowa, Missouri.
† North Dakota, South Dakota, Kansas, and Nebraska.

Source: Calculated from *Livestock and Meat Statistics*, 1957, p. 106.

Appendix Table 26. Percentage of Total Pigs Saved by Region,
Spring and Fall, 1946–1955 Average, and 1957

	Spring		*Fall*		*Total*	
Region	*1946–55*	*1957*	*1946–55*	*1957*	*1946–55*	*1957*
North East	1.8%	1.6%	2.4%	1.8%	2.0%	1.7%
New England	.3	.2	.4	.3	.3	.3
Middle Atlantic	1.5	1.4	2.0	1.5	1.7	1.4
North Central	78.0	77.6	69.9	74.7	74.9	76.4
East North Central	28.2	30.4	33.4	35.0	30.3	32.3
West North Central	49.8	47.2	36.5	39.7	44.6	44.1
South	17.6	18.9	24.8	21.2	20.4	19.8
South Atlantic	7.2	8.5	10.0	9.2	8.3	8.8
East South Central	5.8	6.9	8.4	8.0	6.8	7.3
West South Central	4.6	3.5	6.4	4.0	5.3	3.7
West	2.5	2.0	3.0	2.3	2.7	2.1
Mountain	1.3	1.0	1.5	1.0	1.4	1.0
Pacific	1.2	1.0	1.5	1.3	1.3	1.1
Total United States	100.0%	100.0%	100.0%	100.0%	100.0%	100.0%

Source: Calculated from *Livestock and Meat Statistics*, 1957, pp.
26–27.

Appendix Table 27.   Hog Production, 1954 and 1957, and Average Number of Hogs Sold per Farm, 1944 and 1954, by Region

Region	% of Total U.S. Hog Production *		Average No. of Hogs Sold per Farm		
	1954	1957	1944	1954	% Change
North East	1.8%	1.6%	17	25	53%
New England	.3	.3	16	38	138
Middle Atlantic	1.5	1.3	17	24	41
North Central	80.7	78.0	43	57	33
East North Central	31.5	32.8	41	55	34
West North Central	49.2	46.0	45	58	39
South	15.5	17.6	15	16	7
South Atlantic	6.8	7.5	16	17	6
East South Central	5.5	6.7	16	16	0
West South Central	3.2	3.4	14	14	0
West	2.0	2.0	29	29	0
Mountain	1.0	1.0	25	21	−16
Pacific	1.0	1.0	37	42	14
Total United States	100.0	100.0	32	40	24

* Liveweight production.

Source: U. S. Agricultural Research Service, Statistical Bulletin No. 184, *Meat Animals, Farm Production, Disposition, and Income, 1950–1954* (Washington, Government Printing Office, June 1956), p. 25, *Census of Agriculture, 1954* (Washington, Government Printing Office), p. 509, and *Livestock and Meat Situation, 1957*, p. 16, and *Livestock and Meat Statistics*, July 1958, p. 45.

Appendix Table 28. Percentage of Total U. S. Hog Slaughter by Region, 1947–1957

	North East			North Central			South				West		
Year	New England	Middle Atlantic	Total N.E.	E.N. Central	W.N. Central	Total N. Central	South Atlantic	E.S. Central	W.S. Central	Total South	Mountain	Pacific	Total West
1957	1.1%	8.5%	9.6%	26.3%	39.5%	65.8%	9.0%	5.5%	4.0%	18.5%	2.0%	4.1%	6.1%
1956	1.1	8.1	9.2	25.8	40.7	66.5	8.4	5.0	4.3	17.7	2.0	4.6	6.6
1955	1.2	8.2	9.4	25.6	41.6	67.2	8.0	4.7	4.2	16.9	2.0	4.5	6.5
1954	1.3	8.5	9.8	26.5	40.7	67.2	8.3	4.4	4.1	16.8	2.0	4.2	6.2
1953	1.2	8.4	9.6	27.2	39.7	66.9	8.6	4.5	4.0	17.1	2.1	4.3	6.4
1952	1.2	8.4	9.6	27.1	39.2	66.3	8.1	4.5	4.6	17.2	2.2	4.7	6.9
1951	1.2	8.0	9.2	27.7	39.9	67.6	7.4	4.4	4.5	16.3	2.2	4.7	6.9
1950	1.2	8.3	9.5	27.4	40.6	68.0	7.1	4.2	4.2	15.5	2.3	4.7	7.0
1949	1.3	8.2	9.5	27.7	41.0	68.7	6.8	3.9	4.1	14.8	2.3	4.7	7.0
1948	1.3	8.2	9.5	29.0	38.9	67.9	7.4	3.8	4.9	16.1	1.9	4.6	6.5
1947	1.5	8.5	10.0	28.2	40.1	68.3	7.4	3.4	4.5	15.3	2.0	4.4	6.4

Source: Calculated from *Livestock and Meat Statistics*, 1957, p. 108.

Appendix Table 29. Percentage of Lambs Saved by Region, 1946–1955 Average and 1957

Region	As a % of U.S. Total		As a % of Ewes 1 Year Old or Older	
	Average 1946–55	1957	Average 1946–55	1957
Northeast	1.5%	1.8%	97%	101%
New England	.2	.3	93	92
Middle Atlantic	1.3	1.5	97	103
North Central	28.3	32.6	103	107
East North Central	10.1	10.6	103	104
West North Central	18.2	22.0	103	109
South	24.1	21.2	78	81
South Atlantic	3.1	3.5	108	106
East South Central	4.6	4.6	109	103
West South Central	16.4	13.1	69	74
West	46.0	44.4	88	92
Mountain	35.1	33.5	86	90
Pacific	10.9	10.9	96	98
Total United States	100.0%	100.0%	89%	94%

Source: Calculated from *Livestock and Meat Statistics*, 1957, p. 25.

Appendix Table 30. Feed Units of All Feed, Including Pasture, Consumed per Head, or per Unit of Production, Beef Cattle, Hogs, Sheep and Lambs, and Broilers, Selected Years, 1930–1956

| | Beef Cattle | | | | | | | |
Year	Grain Fattened per Head	Other Cattle per Head	Cattle Calves/ 100# Pro- duced *	Hogs/ 100# Pro- duced	Sheep & Lambs per Head	Broilers per Head	per 100# Prod.	Index †
1956	6,201	3,446	963	536	798	9.8	312	100
1955	6,070	3,067	896	514	707	10.2	317	95
1954	6,053	3,187	898	494	751	10.4	339	95
1953	5,783	3,116	878	538	722	10.8	351	96
1952	5,391	3,197	922	477	744	11.0	358	96
1951	6,129	3,370	980	533	751	11.2	366	101
1950	5,927	3,490	955	522	780	11.5	374	100
1945	5,579	3,336	994	592	782	13.9	459	105
1940	4,408	3,483	1,010	523	804	14.3	489	100
1935	3,889	2,842	837	542	673	15.1	528	93
1930	3,559	3,069	877	504	700	—	—	90

* Feed for all cattle except milk cows divided by net live weight production of cattle and calves. Growth of dairy heifers and calves is included.

† Feed per production unit all livestock, excluding horses and mules, 1947–1949 = 100.

Source: *Consumption of Feed by Livestock, 1909–56*, pp. 126, 127, and U. S. Agriculture Research Service, Report 43–103, *Livestock Production Units* (Washington, Government Printing Office, June 1959), p. 16.

Appendix Table 31. Number of Producers and Head of Livestock on Hand and Sold by Type of Farm, 1954

	Farms		Livestock		Livestock per Farm
	Number	%	Number	%	Number
Cattle and Calves					
On Farms	3,650,714	100%	95,027,041	100%	26.0
Noncommercial	1,023,755	28	6,183,077	6	6.0
Commercial	2,626,959	72	88,843,964	94	33.8
Commercial Livestock	657,313	18	42,651,757	45	64.9
Sold	2,611,031	100%	44,350,808	100%	17.0
Noncommercial	442,541	17	1,760,146	4	4.0
Commercial	2,168,490	83	42,590,662	96	19.6
Commercial Livestock	644,200	25	24,883,618	56	38.6
Hogs and Pigs					
On Farms	2,365,708	100%	57,092,919	100%	24.1
Noncommercial	573,241	24	2,129,373	4	3.7
Commercial	1,792,467	76	54,963,546	96	30.7
Commercial Livestock	480,983	20	31,933,544	56	66.4
Sold	1,423,943	100%	57,418,588	100%	40.3
Noncommercial	168,388	12	779,338	1	4.6
Commercial	1,255,555	88	56,641,238	99	45.1
Commercial Livestock	454,985	32	36,539,157	64	80.3
Sheep					
On Farms	361,001 *	100%	31,618,909 *	100%	87.6
Noncommercial	57,445	16	1,442,471	5	25.0
Commercial	303,556	84	30,176,438	95	99.4
Commercial Livestock	133,061	37	23,032,540	73	173.1
Sold	289,118 *	100%	22,335,858 *	100%	77.2
Noncommercial	29,365	10	n		
Commercial	259,762	90	n		
Commercial Livestock	124,484	43	n	n	

* Florida, Georgia, and South Carolina not included.
n Not Available.

Source: 1954 Census of Agriculture, Volume II, Chapter VI, pp. 433, 434, 441, 472, 504; and Volume III, part 8, pp. 31, 32.

Appendix Table 32. Average Weights of Barrows and Gilts, Chicago, Monthly, 1947–1957

Year	Jan.	Feb.	Mar.	Apr.	May	June	July	Aug.	Sept.	Oct.	Nov.	Dec.	Average
1957	241	236	236	235	239	235	224	215	215	222	228	232	230
1956	241	239	235	233	231	230	227	219	219	221	227	245	231
1955	250	250	246	244	241	235	228	220	215	219	227	234	235
1954	245	244	246	249	246	243	235	218	217	226	235	243	238
1953	242	237	236	236	232	229	226	216	211	216	226	233	230
1952	238	245	246	242	238	233	231	230	223	222	228	236	235
1951	244	240	242	240	239	238	234	228	217	219	225	232	234
1950	247	250	244	246	250	242	238	235	220	225	229	236	239
1949	255	254	256	250	257	250	242	231	215	222	232	239	242
1948	255	260	267	267	271	275	253	239	232	226	234	245	254
1947	248	256	263	261	267	263	261	259	239	225	231	240	249

Source: *Livestock and Meat Statistics*, 1957, p. 183.

Appendix Table 33. Carcass Beef Officially Graded and Grade Marked by U. S. Department of Agriculture, 1957

(In Thousands of Pounds)

Month	Prime	Choice	Good	Standard	Commercial	Utility	Cutter	Canner	Total
Jan.	32,067	366,498	181,318	26,837	13,638	22,228	3,268	360	646,214
Feb.	27,487	321,451	161,370	20,742	9,556	15,698	2,305	359	558,968
Mar.	29,329	340,404	170,668	22,354	9,344	12,706	2,494	377	587,675
Apr.	28,631	328,370	153,445	21,784	9,299	10,218	2,184	482	554,413
May	30,866	379,722	155,569	22,614	9,222	10,982	2,988	396	612,358
June	27,130	334,518	141,522	22,029	7,826	11,755	2,612	533	547,927
July	31,006	355,654	152,866	21,483	9,354	15,681	2,963	573	589,580
Aug.	33,231	360,114	160,784	22,634	10,443	14,354	3,184	551	605,296
Sept.	30,751	331,003	150,146	22,835	9,321	11,892	3,216	737	559,901
Oct.	33,767	372,446	166,079	22,799	8,444	9,296	3,967	723	617,520
Nov.	32,345	305,179	143,595	19,566	9,768	29,638	4,430	2,107	546,629
Dec.	29,476	301,577	145,646	17,522	8,520	9,914	3,340	436	516,431
Total	366,085	4,096,936	1,883,008	263,200	114,735	174,363	36,952	7,633	6,942,912
(%)	5.3%	59.0%	27.1%	3.8%	1.7%	2.5%	.5%	.1%	100.0%

Source: *Livestock and Meat Statistics, 1957*, p. 299. Percentages calculated.

Appendix Table 34. Average Hourly Earnings for Selected Types of United States Farming Areas, Average 1947–1949 and 1954–1957

Type of Farming Area	Average 1947–49	1954	1955	1956	1957 *
Dairy farms, eastern Wisconsin	.73	.48	.39	.54	.52
Hog-dairy farms, Corn Belt	1.18	1.25	.68	.87	.99
Hog-beef raising farms, Corn Belt	.80	.49	.50	.51	.66
Hog-beef fattening farms, Corn Belt	2.37	1.92	.57	1.29	1.46
Cash grain farms, Corn Belt	2.20	1.82	1.10	1.92	.66
Wheat-small grain-livestock farms, Northern Plains	2.18	.16	1.66	2.05	.55
Wheat-corn-livestock farms, Northern Plains	1.48	.51	.25	.47	.81
Wheat-roughage-livestock farms, Northern Plains	1.57	.39	.81	.37	.66
Winter wheat farms, Southern Plains	3.34	1.94	.89	.34	.82
Sheep ranches, Northern Plains livestock area	.97	.26	.31	.65	1.67
Cattle ranches, Northern Plains livestock area	1.14	.29	.03	−.26	.20
Cattle ranches, Intermountain region	1.47	.50	.50	.75	1.31
Sheep ranches, Southwest	.15	−2.29	−1.43	−2.37	−1.16
Cattle ranches, Southwest	.73	−1.92	−.84	−2.49	−.69
Poultry farms, New Jersey	.93	−.72	.13	−.14	−.29

* Preliminary.

Source: U. S. Agricultural Research Service, Agriculture Information Bulletin No. 176, *Farm Costs and Returns* (Washington, Government Printing Office, Revised June 1958), pp. 46–76.

Appendix Table 35.   Government Price-Assistance Purchases of Surplus Meat and Lard, 1951–1958, with Section 32 Funds (In Millions of Pounds and Millions of Dollars)

Year Beginning	Beef		Pork		Lard		Total	
	Quantity	Value	Quantity	Value	Quantity	Value	Quantity	Value
July,								
1958	0	0	0	0	0	0	0	0
1957	17 *	$ 7 *	0	0	0	0	17	$ 7
1956	72	26	6	$ 4	22	$4	100	34
1955	12 †	4 †	158	95	39	6	219	105
1954	0	0	0	0	0	0	0	0
1953	213	84	0	0	0	0	213	84
1952	4	1	0	0	0	0	4	1
1951	0	0	31 ‡	15 ‡	0	0	31	15

* Section 6 expenditures of $7 million for 17 million pounds.
† Section 6 expenditures of $4 million for 112 million pounds.
‡ Section 6 expenditures of $3 million for 8 million pounds.

Source: *Livestock and Meat Situation*, November 1957, p. 32., and Harold Briemyer, U. S. Department of Agriculture.

Appendix Table 36. Programmed and Actual Exports of Meat and Meat Products under Title I of Public Law 480 * (Sales for Foreign Currency), January 1955–September 1958
(In Thousands of Dollars and Thousands of Pounds)

| | | Exports | | | | | | | |
| | Programmed Exports, Value All | Beef | | Pork | | Lard | | Tallow | |
Country of Destination	Products	Quantity	Value	Quantity	Value	Quantity	Value	Quantity	Value
Austria	$ 4,397					23,054	$ 2,400		
Brazil	6,840					16,383	2,220		
Chile	1,090								
China (Taiwan)	1,000							10,233	$ 723
Ecuador	540							2,489	249
Greece						22	3		
Israel	10,100	24,792	$ 6,197						
Korea	8,000			9,631	$4,815			1,058	95
Paraguay	195					1,473	186		
Philippines	1,000								
Poland	2,800							30,210	2,417
Spain	22,702	50,720	12,754	4,755	1,700			53,018	4,800
Turkey	8,800	12,085	3,140					43,865	3,948
Yugoslavia	21,700					142,707	18,217	21,488	1,719
Total 1/55–9/57	$89,164	87,597	$22,091	14,386	$6,515	183,639	$23,026	162,361	$13,951
1/55–9/58		90415,	23,200	14,386	6,515	186,380	23,500	183,657	16,200

* No meat, lard, or tallow has been exported under other Titles.

Source: *Livestock and Meat Situation*, November 8, 1957, p. 30, and data provided by the Foreign Agricultural Service. Totals for January 1955 to September 1958 from correspondence with Agricultural Marketing Service personnel.

BIBLIOGRAPHY

American Meat Institute, *Financial Facts About the Meat Packing Industry, 1957* (Chicago, July 1958).

American Restaurant Magazine, "American Restaurant Subscriber Analysis" (Chicago, 1958).

Barton, G. T., and Daly, R. F., "Prospects for Agriculture in a Growing Economy," address at the Conference on Problems and Policies of American Agriculture at Iowa State College, Ames, Iowa, October 27–31, 1958.

Bauman, Ronald, "Comparable Costs of Portable and Permanent Structures in Swine Production and the Effect of Intensity of Use on Costs," *Some Considerations in Intensified Systems of Hog Production*, Mimeo ID-19, Purdue University, Lafayette, Indiana, April 17, 1957.

Cochrane, Willard, *Farm Prices—Myth and Reality* (Minneapolis, University of Minnesota Press, 1958).

Ezekiel, M. J. B., "The Cobweb Theorem," *Quarterly Journal of Economics*, February 1938.

Fortune Magazine, "The Future Population Mix," February 1959.

Harvard Business School, Division of Research, Bulletin No. 148, *Operating Results of Food Chains in 1957*, by Wilbur B. England.

Institution Magazine, "The Institutional Market for Food Products" (Chicago, 1958).

Kelley, W. T., "Specification Buying by the Large Retailer," *Journal of Marketing*, January 1954.

Kramer, R. C., "Cattle Feeding by and for Packers and Retailers," a report to the research director of The Fact-Finding Committee of the American National Cattlemen's Association, July 1959.

Life Study of Consumer Expenditures, Supplement (New York, Time Incorporated, 1958).

Luby, P., "Declining Demand for Pork—Reconsideration of Causes and Suggested Prescription for Remedy," *Journal of Farm Economics*, December 1958.

Mehren, G., "How Is the Market Made in Integrated Industries?"

Address before the National Institute of Animal Agriculture, Lafayette, Indiana, April 21, 1958.

National Food Situation (Washington, Government Printing Office, July 1958).

Ohio Agricultural Experiment Station, Research Bulletin No. 846, *Livestock Marketing in the North Central Region*, Part 1, "Where Farmers and Ranchers Buy and Sell," by R. R. Newberg (Wooster, Ohio, December 1959).

Progressive Grocer, "Facts in Grocery Distribution," annual editions 1953–1959.

———, unpublished survey, 1959.

Reeve, Lewis, et al., *More Swine Dollars from Multiple Farrowing* (Chicago, American Meat Institute, 1957).

Schneider, Elliot, *The Meat Packing Industry* (New York, Paine, Webber, Jackson & Curtis, July 1958).

Shepherd, Geoffrey S., *Marketing Farm Products* (Ames, Iowa State College Press, 3rd edition, 1955).

South Dakota Experiment Station, Bulletin No. 365, *Marketing Livestock in the Corn Belt Region*, November 1942.

South Dakota State College, Extension Circular No. 434, "Will the Meat Type Hog Pay?" by E. Dailey and L. Bender (Brookings, South Dakota State College, May 1952).

Stewart, H. L., "Prospects for Adjustment in Production and Resource Use," address at the 36th Annual Outlook Conference of the U. S. Agricultural Marketing Service, Farm Economics Research Division, Washington, November 18, 1958.

Super Market Institute, *Super Market Industry Speaks* (Chicago, 1954, 1956, 1957, 1958 editions).

Super Market Merchandising, April 1959.

Texas Agricultural Experiment Station, Miscellaneous Publication No. 93, "Texas Livestock Auction Markets—Methods and Facilities" (College Station, April 1953).

———, Miscellaneous Publication No. 118, "Texas Livestock Auction Markets" (College Station, December 1954).

This Week Magazine, "Supermarketing USA, 1957" (New York, 1958).

Topics Publishing Company, "What the Public Spends for Grocery Store Products" (New York, 1958).

U. S. Department of Agriculture, Agricultural Marketing Service, Agriculture Handbook No. 83, "Charting the Seasonal Market for Meat Animals," by Harold Breimyer and Charlotte A. Kause (Washington, Government Printing Office, March 1956).

———, ———, Bulletin No. 96, "Price Elasticities of Demand for Nondurable Goods, with Emphasis on Food," by Richard J. Foote (Washington, Government Printing Office, March 1956).

———, ———, Bulletin No. 249, "Consumption Patterns for Meat," by Harold Breimyer and Charlotte A. Kause (Washington, Government Printing Office, May 1958).

———, ———, *Livestock and Meat Situation,* March 1958, May 1958, September 1958, November 1958, March 1959 (Washington, Government Printing Office).

———, ———, Marketing Research Report No. 216, "Market Outlets for Livestock Producers," by Victor B. Phillips and Gerald Engelman (Washington, Government Printing Office, March 1958).

———, ———, Marketing Research Report No. 223, "Livestock Auction Markets in the United States," by Gerald Engelman and Betty Sue Pence (Washington, Government Printing Office, March 1958).

———, ———, Marketing Research Report No. 298, "Economic Effects of U. S. Grades for Beef," by Willard F. Williams et al. (Washington, Government Printing Office, January 1959).

———, ———, Marketing Research Report No. 299, "Livestock Terminal Markets in the United States," by Edward Uvacek and Dalton L. Wilson (Washington, Government Printing Office, January 1959).

———, ———, "Number of Livestock Slaughter Establishments, March 1, 1950" (Washington, Government Printing Office, 1954).

———, ———, "Number of Slaughtering Establishments, March 1, 1955" (Washington Government Printing Office, 1959).

———, ———, Packers and Stockyards Docket No. 16, "Feeding Operations of Meat Packers" (Washington, Government Printing Office, September 1958).

———, ———, Statistical Bulletin No. 230, "Livestock and Meat

Statistics, 1957" (Washington, Government Printing Office, July 1958).

——, Agricultural Research Service, Agriculture Handbook No. 62, "Supplement for 1956 to Consumption of Food in the United States, 1909–52" (Washington, Government Printing Office, September 1957).

——, ——, Agriculture Handbook No. 62, "Supplement for 1957 to Consumption of Food in the United States, 1909–52" (Washington, Government Printing Office, August 1958).

——, ——, Agriculture Information Bulletin No. 140, "Agricultural Land Resources in the United States, with Special Reference to Present and Potential Cropland and Pastures," by Hugh H. Wooten and James R. Anderson (Washington, Government Printing Office, June 1955).

——, ——, Agriculture Information Bulletin No. 176, "Farm Costs and Returns" (Washington, Government Printing Office, Revised, June 1958).

——, ——, Production Research Report No. 21, "Consumption of Feed by Livestock, 1909–56," by R. D. Jennings (Washington, Government Printing Office, November 1958).

——, ——, Report 43–103, "Livestock Production Units," by Earl F. Hodges (Washington, Government Printing Office, June 1959).

——, ——, Statistical Bulletin No. 184, "Meat Animals, Farm Production, Disposition and Income, 1950–1954" (Washington, Government Printing Office, June 1956).

——, ——, Statistical Bulletin No. 233 and Supplement I, "Changes in Farm Production and Efficiency" (Washington, Government Printing Office, August 1958).

——, Agricultural Statistics, 1957 (Washington, Government Printing Office, 1958).

——, Farmer Cooperative Service, General Report No. 29, "Farmer Meat Packing Enterprises in the United States," by R. L. Fox (Washington, Government Printing Office, April 1957).

——, ——, General Report No. 39, "Improving Livestock Marketing Efficiency," by Ira Stevens and R. L. Fox (Washington, Government Printing Office, January 1958).

———, ———, General Report No. 48, "Statistics for Farmer Co-operatives, 1955–56," by Anne Gessner (Washington, Government Printing Office, July 1958).

———, "Farmer in a Changing World," *Yearbook of Agriculture 1940* (Washington, Government Printing Office, 1940).

———, "Marketing," *Yearbook of Agriculture 1954* (Washington, Government Printing Office, 1954).

U. S. Department of Commerce, Bureau of the Census, "1954 Census of Agriculture" (Washington, Government Printing Office, 1956).

———, ———, Current Population Reports P-25, No. 63 (Washington, Government Printing Office, November 2, 1955).

———, ———, Current Population Reports P-25, No. 187 (Washington, Government Printing Office, November 10, 1958).

———, ———, Current Population Reports P-25, No. 191 (Washington, Government Printing Office, December 11, 1958).

U. S. Congress, Subcommittee on Agricultural Policy, Joint Economic Committee, *The Policy for Commercial Agriculture, Its Relation to Economic Growth and Stability*, "Current Imbalance of Supply and Demand for Farm Products," by M. R. Benedict, and "Prospective Demands for Food and Fiber," by R. F. Daly, 85th Congress, 1st Session (Washington, Government Printing Office, November 1957).

U. S. Senate, Hearings before the Subcommittee on Antitrust and Monopoly of the Committee on the Judiciary, "Unfair Trade Practices in the Meat Industry," 85th Congress, 1st Session (Washington, Government Printing Office, May 1957).

———, Report of the Subcommittee on Antitrust and Monopoly to the Committee on the Judiciary, "Concentration in American Industry" (Washington, Government Printing Office, 1957).

U.S. *v.* Swift and Company, "Affidavits of Swift Defendants in Opposition to Motion of United States for Summary Judgment," in the United States District Court for the Northern District of Illinois, Eastern Division, May 1958.

———, "Brief by the United States in Support of Motion for Summary Judgment," Equity No. 37623, in the United States District Court for the District of Columbia (mimeographed, undated).

Voluntary and Cooperative Group Magazine, April 1959.

Williams, Willard F., "Structural Changes in the Meat Industry," *Journal of Farm Economics*, May 1958.

Wingate, John, *Buying for Retail Stores* (New York, Prentice-Hall, 1956).

Working, Elmer, *Demand for Meat* (Chicago, Institute of Meat Packing, 1954).